SECRET
67

B
BottomLineBooks
BottomLineInc.com

Bottom Line Books is an imprint of Bottom Line Inc., publisher of print periodicals, e-letters and books. We are dedicated to bringing you the best information from the most knowledgeable sources in the world. Our goal is to help you gain greater wealth, better health, more wisdom, extra time and increased happiness.

Printed in the United States of America

YB/am

Contents

3. Travel and Entertainment Secrets

4. Super Savings for Home and Family

5. Health and Happiness Secrets

6. Tax Savvy

Super Money-Making Secrets

Warren Buffett's Secrets to Making Money In Good Times and Bad

I have spent thousands of hours with legendary Nebraskan investor Warren Buffett, chairman and CEO of the conglomerate Berkshire Hathaway. While I was writing his biography, he gave me unprecedented access to his work, opinions, struggles, triumphs, follies and wisdom. Buffett's success on Wall Street has made him the richest man in the world. But in many ways, he's closer to Main Street than Wall Street, a careful investor like you and me who still lives in the house he bought in 1958 for $31,500.

In grim markets, he has been at his most brilliant and visionary. No one has a better record of protecting assets, making shrewd purchases—and inspiring the confidence we need to survive financial turmoil.

Advice Buffett is giving to White House Cabinet secretaries— and secretaries in his own offices in Omaha…

• **Invest in what you understand.** In the years 1998 to 2000, Buffett famously avoided buying Internet stocks because he didn't see how the companies could make enough money to justify their valuations. In 2002, he started warning against complicated "derivatives," including the subprime mortgage deals that have devastated such giants as the investment firm Lehman Brothers and insurer AIG—deals that are at the core of the financial crisis.

If you want an understandable business, Buffett points to Coca-Cola, of which he owns about 9%. After 128 years, the Coca-Cola Company still sells more than a billion beverage servings a day. He also is partial to Gillette, a division of Procter & Gamble (P&G). He holds a 2% stake in P&G. Gillette dominates US razor blade sales, and it will never run out of customers as it expands worldwide.

- **Decide on your investing values and criteria—then maintain them no matter how good or bad the market is.** When investors get in trouble, it's usually because fear or greed has made them ignore commonsense rules.

Buffett has strategies that he follows in bull and bear markets. He looks for quality companies with ethical, highly committed management teams in essential but often unexciting industries. Most important, he waits for a time when he can acquire these companies at a large discount, often 40% below what he considers their "fair values."

- **Have cash on hand.** Many investors feel that they need to be fully invested and that holding cash in a portfolio is a drag on returns. Cash, however, has its advantages when markets plunge. For several years, Buffett sat on more than $44 billion of cash in Berkshire Hathaway accounts. This allowed him in September 2008 to brilliantly and carefully pick up shares of preferred stocks from General Electric and Goldman Sachs in specially negotiated deals with hefty dividends and at nearly half off the price they had been selling for a few months earlier.

- **Don't try to catch a falling knife until you have a handle on the risk.** Many investors get into trouble because they see opportunity But don't think about risk fully enough. Asking yourself, "And then what?" over and over can help you see all the possible consequences. Let me give you one example from Buffett's life. In spring 2008, Buffett was approached about investing in, or perhaps even buying, Bear Stearns. Until it was badly damaged by the recent subprime mortgage debacle, Bear Stearns was one of the world's largest global investment banks and brokerage firms.

Buffett could have practically named his terms, but he passed on the deal. He worried that the company had at least 750,000 derivative investments. He said that even if he cloned Albert Einstein and worked 12-hour days with him, they could never properly analyze the risk of that many investments. Rebuffed by Buffett, Bear Stearns raised billions in capital from sovereign wealth funds in China and the Middle East. Those funds lost most of their money as Bear Stearns unraveled and was eventually taken over by JPMorgan Chase.

- **Don't bet the ranch.** As an investor, leave yourself a margin of safety in case something goes very wrong. Buffet says that over the past 50 years, he never permanently lost more than 2% of his own personal worth on any investment position. He has suffered heavy losses at times, but only on paper, which is why he warns against using leverage (borrowing money to increase your bet on a stock pick).

- **You can't be just a little bit smart.** Buffett feels that if you try to be just a little bit smart, you're liable to be really dumb, especially in a treacherous market. Few people have the time or inclination to study enough to beat the market. Diversification is probably your best route. Choose a low-cost index fund, and put your money into it slowly and steadily over time. With this strategy you won't buy everything at the wrong price or at the wrong time.

- **Never sell into a panic, such as the one in 2008.** Buffett isn't very worried about the big picture for America. He believes that the stock market does some very crazy things in the short run, but in the long run, it behaves quite rationally.

Buffett's underlying belief now is that the American economy will do very well and so will people who own a piece of it. There are a lot of factors gumming up its potential now. But 10 years from now, he says, we'll look back and see that, as investors, we could have made some extraordinary buys.

Alice Schroeder, a former Wall Street analyst and former managing director at Morgan Stanley, New York City. She is author of *The Snowball: Warren Buffett and the Business of Life* (Bantam).

REPORT #2

Free Gas Just for You

Beat the high cost at the pumps. You can receive up to $200 in free gas per month through the FreeGasHelp.com program.

The concept is simple...your vehicle advertises products or services and you get free gas. There is a wide range of advertising options that you can choose from—including door magnets, window decals, license plate frames and complete vehicle wraps.

To qualify, you need to drive at least 1,000 miles a month, your vehicle needs to be in good condition and you need to be its registered owner. Log on to *www.freegashelp.com* for more information.

REPORT #3

Refuse to Lose in the Stock Market

Consider the following example...if a stock is priced at $100/share, buy put options that give you the right to sell the stock at $90/share within 12 or 24 months. Then sell call options, which let someone else have the right to buy your stock at $120/share over the same period. This structure is called a collar.

The cost of the put and the proceeds from the call should be equal to limit your downside and ensure you get at least $90 a share. If the stock price falls below $90, you still can sell it for $90. If it rises above $120, you can sell it or buy back the call option.

Caution: Options trading is complex—be sure to consult a knowledgeable financial adviser.

Christopher Cordaro, CFP, CFA , RegentAtlantic Capital LLC, Morristown, New Jersey, *www.regentatlantic.com.*

REPORT #4

Turn Your Junk into Cash

Whether you are downsizing or you just inherited a house full of antiques, here are the best ways to sell items that you don't need or want—and for a tidy sum...

Consignment Shops

Wares typically include clothing, furs, china, collectibles and furniture. The owner of the shop establishes the price. You pay no penalty if your items fail to sell, but they may not be sold for months. You can expect to get about 50% of the sale price. *Smart selling strategies...*

• **Choose a shop in an upscale neighborhood** to get the highest possible price.

• **Be sure to get price estimates from several shops**—figures can vary widely.

Estate Sales/Garage Sales

These are best for less expensive possessions that you want to sell quickly. *Smart selling strategies...*

• **Advertise the sale in the newspaper.**

• **Restrict the sale to certain areas in your house.** Keep more valuable items in a glass case or locked cabinet. Shoplifters frequent estate sales.

• **Expect to haggle.** Most buyers will offer 20% less than your asking price but eventually will compromise at 10% less.

• **Hire a professional estate or tag sale organizer** if you have many high-quality possessions. They have large mail and e-mail lists that will attract active buyers. They also can advise you objectively on how to price items and will handle any haggling.

Expect to keep 75% of the proceeds. To find an organizer for your sale, check the National Association of Professional Organizers, 856-380-6828, *www.napo.net.*

Internet Auctions

These Web sites are great for disposing of specialized items or small items—appliances, clothing, sporting goods and computer equipment—that wouldn't fetch very much at a garage sale.

Online auctions require time and/or effort—you must photograph items, write descriptions and ship them to buyers— but costs are reasonable. At *www.ebay.com*, the most popular site, you pay a small fee to list items and a percentage of the closing price if they sell. Visit the eBay Web site for details.

Worthwhile reading: *How to Sell Anything on eBay*...and *Make a Fortune!* by Dennis Prince (McGraw-Hill). *Smart selling strategies...*

• **Make sure your auction begins and ends on a weekend—when online activity is brisk.** If you have many items to sell and need storage space, try Portable On Demand Storage (PODS), which, unlike other storage centers, will deliver storage containers directly to your home. You fill the containers, and they are then taken to a local climate-controlled facility that you can access. You can rent a 7-, 12- or 16-foot-long container (all are 8 feet tall), large enough to hold the contents of a single-family home. Cost depends on location and container size, plus there's a charge for initial delivery and final pickup of the container.

For information and to see if this service is available in your area: 877-770-7637, *www.pods.com.*

Auction Houses

These are good for selling valuable antiques, art and jewelry with little effort. The price you pay for ease of sale is the extra cost and wasted time if the item doesn't sell. You're more likely to attract an auction house's interest if you have many valuable items instead of one or two trinkets. An auction representative will appraise the items in your home and transport them to the auction house. After all the fees and commissions, you will wind up with about 50% to 75% of the sale price.

Major auction houses include: Bonhams (*www.bonhams. com*)...Christie's (*www.christies.com*)...Doyle New York (*www. doylenewyork.com*)...and Sotheby's (*www.sothebys.com*). *Smart selling strategies...*

• **Do your own research.** Few people realize that auction houses can be persuaded to increase their appraisals. How to convince them? Prove that similar items recently have been auctioned for higher prices. Say, for instance, you have a 19th-century cherry desk, call around and find another auction house that has sold one and ask for a catalog.

Cost: $10 to $50 or more per catalog.

Also helpful: Antiques Roadshow Primer and *Antiques Roadshow Collectibles* both by Carol Prisant (both from Workman). *Kovels' Antiques and Collectibles Price Guide* by Terry Kovel and Kim Kovel (Black Dog & Leventhal).

• **Negotiate fees.** Auction houses may reduce or eliminate charges, depending on how badly they want your items.

- **Check your insurance coverage.** Most homeowner's policies cover any of your items while they are at the auction house. Otherwise, you'll pay 2% of the value for temporary insurance coverage.

Adriane G. Berg, elder law attorney, Lebanon, New Jersey, and New York City, and a founder of the National Academy of Elder Law Attorneys. She is author of many books on personal finance, including *How Not to Go Broke at 102! Achieving Everlasting Wealth* (Wiley). Her Web site is *www.adrianeberg.us*.

REPORT #5

Low-Cost Home Businesses That Pay Big Bucks

You can start a successful business without a lot of start-up capital. I identified 1,500 people who earn $50,000 or more each year from businesses they founded with an initial investment of $100 or less. *Their secrets...*

Sell Information

Most successful $100 start-ups sell information. Unlike most businesses, information providers typically don't require expensive inventory, equipment, employees or leases.

What information should you sell? If you're an expert in some aspect of your profession, that's likely to be your best bet. *If not, ask yourself...*

- **What's a task that many people consider inscrutable and aggravating that I understand and enjoy?** People are happy to pay those who can help to alleviate their major annoyances.

Example: Most people consider redeeming airline frequent-flier miles to be extremely frustrating. Gary Leff, the CFO of a Virginia University research center, enjoyed the challenge of mastering his frequent-flier miles. He began charging other travelers $150 per trip to help them get the most from their miles. This second job recently earned him an annual $75,000 in his spare time. *www.BookYourAward.com*

- **What knowledge have I obtained by pursuing my interests that others might pay for?** The knowledge you've acquired might be salable.

Example: Ireland native Benny Lewis became adept at learning foreign languages while traveling. He created a successful Web site and guidebook sharing his strategy for achieving fluency quickly. *Fluentin3Months.com*

- **When do I feel I lack the information that I need to make wise decisions?** If others feel the same way, they might be willing to pay you to provide the facts they lack.

Example: Those who use travel-bidding Web sites such as Priceline.com typically must blindly guess at what bids might be accepted. The Web sites *BiddingforTravel.com* and *BetterBidding.com* were created to help people gather the information they need to place more informed bids.

- **What do people ask for my help with?** If friends and family solicit your guidance on a topic, people you don't know might be willing to pay for it.

Example: A California man named Brett Kelly realized that people were asking for his help with Evernote (a note-taking software program that he used) in part because there was no English-language guide to the program. He wrote *Evernote Essentials*, an eBook that has generated more than $100,000 in sales so far.

- **What information could I provide that would be useful to those participating in a new fad?** If something is new and popular, there might not yet be many resources available for those interested in it.

Example: The trendy Paleo diet (which mimics the diet of our hunter-gatherer ancestors) can be difficult to follow. Jason Glaspey of Portland, Oregon, launched *PaleoPlan.com*, a Web site that offers meal plans, grocery lists and other helpful resources.

How to Make Money

Decide how you will make money from the information you provide. *Low-cost alternatives include...*

- **Serving as a consultant or instructor.**

- **Writing and selling an eBook**—Amazon.com's Kindle Direct Publishing charges no up-front costs to publish eBooks (*http://KDP.Amazon.com*).

- **Launching a Web site or blog,** then selling ads on it or providing links to Internet retailer Web sites that provide commissions—Amazon.com's Associates program pays up to 10% (*http://Affiliate-Program.Amazon.com*).

Test the Market

Test the market for your idea before devoting much time to it. Two low-cost ways to make sure that there's as much demand for your idea as you think...

- **Contact people you consider potential customers.** Ask if they would be interested in what you intend to provide...if there's any other related information or service that they would consider to be even more helpful...and what their biggest challenges and questions are in regard to this area. To locate these potential customers, brainstorm about where such people would be likely to gather, either in your region or online. If your intended customers are other businesses, simply call some of them.

- **Do a Google search of the keywords someone might enter if he/she were looking for a business such as the one you intend to create.** The results might give you a sense of how many people would be interested in your idea and whether there already are businesses that adequately serve their needs.

Example: If the Google search leads to a lot of questions related to the topic on sites such as *Answers.yahoo.com* but few Web sites are providing adequate answers, you might be on the right track for a new business.

Don't Wait

If there does seem to be a market for your business, don't waste time with endless planning and don't try to achieve perfection before you start to sell. Get your idea into development and then onto the market as quickly as possible. The sooner you start making sales, the sooner you'll start receiving useful feedback from customers about how to refine and improve your offerings.

Example: Map designers Jen Adrion and Omar Noory responded to feedback from their early customers by expanding the range of maps they sold. *www.TheseAreThings.com*

If you go above and beyond for your initial customers, they might even become evangelists for your brand. That word of mouth is one of the most cost-effective ways to grow a young business.

Think Free

Many effective marketing options involve providing things for free...

- **Give freebies to tastemakers.** Send samples of your work to those who have the power to influence others.

Example: Megan Hunt, an Omaha-based dress designer, custom makes dresses for two or three fashion bloggers every year. Those bloggers inevitably are grateful for the freebies and write complimentary posts about her dresses.

- **Write free guest posts on popular Web sites visited by your prospective customers.** Many Web sites are happy to run well-thought-out content from people willing to provide it for free. Those who read your articles are likely to consider you an expert on the topic.

- **Offer free consulting.** Charge nothing (or very little) for information or services that usually come at a price, and you will attract prospective customers who later might hire you.

Example: An unemployed Seattle architect named John Morefield set up a booth in a farmers' market offering "Architecture 5¢." His advice impressed so many prospective clients that he soon had a flourishing freelance practice.

- **Use contests to provide free stuff on your blog.** Hold a drawing for something as simple as a free T-shirt with your company logo and people might submit their e-mail addresses in hopes of winning. Those e-mails are prospective future customers.

Example: I recently received more than 1,000 entries in a drawing for a free copy of my book.

Chris Guillebeau, author of *The $100 Startup: Reinvent the Way You Make a Living, Do What You Love, and Create a New Future* (Crown). Based in Portland, Oregon, he is the founder of The Art of Non-Conformity, a blog about changing the world by achieving personal goals. *www.ChrisGuillebeau.com*

REPORT #6

How to Find Your Dream Job Over 50

If a job interviewer makes age-related assumptions—for instance, that older workers do not get along with younger ones—address the subject directly by saying, "I like to learn from people of all ages." Expect tough questions and have answers ready.

Example: If the interviewer asks why you are applying for a lower-level job than you had in the past, say you enjoyed management but would prefer more hands-on involvement in projects at this point in your career. Tailor your résumé to what employers want—describe your experience in terms of the specific skills desired by the company you are targeting.

Andrea Kay, career consultant and author of *This Is How to Get Your Next Job* (Amacom), quoted online at *MarketWatch.com.*

2

Create Your Dream
Retirement

Say "No" to Nursing Homes

Most people I know are adamant that they want to stay in their homes as long as possible as they grow older. The good news is that there are now many affordable—and sometimes surprising—alternatives to nursing homes. *Best approaches...*

• **Use new technology to stay at home.** For example, you can now buy home medication-dispensing devices that store all your pills, unlock when it's time to take them and alert you with a signal at pill time. These devices are even wired to a remote command center that will call you or a relative if you miss just one dose! In addition, home-care agencies can set up devices (with sensors worn by the patient) for daily monitoring of blood pressure and body temperature.

Recent development: Medicare has recently agreed to cover many such home services for people who otherwise would be placed in a more costly nursing home.

• **Try a "granny apartment."** That's what today's so-called accessory dwelling units (ADUs) were called years ago. An ADU (fully equipped with bathroom and kitchen) is a one-room, freestanding house or a small addition to a relative's home.

Recent development: Years ago, zoning laws in most communities put major restrictions on these units, but that has now changed in many areas. A friend of mine built an addition onto her house (for $65,000—less than the cost of a year in a nursing home) for her mother who had Alzheimer's disease. My friend also used community services, including adult day care and occasional in-home caregiving aides. To learn more about such community services, consult the Administration on Aging's resources Web site, *www.ElderCare.gov*, or call 800-677-1116.

• **Consider "campus" living.** It may not be quite as much fun as a college campus, but assisted-living facilities do offer their own activities (such as bridge, yoga classes and book clubs) and can be ideal for people who can't stay in a traditional home or live with relatives. With assisted living, you have your own apartment and receive three meals a day, medical monitoring and medication assistance (by a nurse or an aide).

Cost: $1,000 to $5,000 per person per month.*

Recent development: Growing numbers of so-called continuing-care communities. They offer independent (often freestanding homes) and assisted-living programs in addition to skilled nursing home services all on the same campus. These communities can be expensive, often requiring a front-end, onetime payment of $100,000 or more, plus monthly fees for meals and other services.

Good to know: Many continuing-care communities now have a variety of payment options to make them more affordable. Go to the AARP Web site, *www.AARP.org*, and search "Caregiving," to research different payment methods.

Charles B. Inlander, consumer advocate and health-care consultant based in Fogelsville, Pennsylvania. He was the founding president of the nonprofit People's Medical Society, a consumer advocacy organization that is credited with key improvements in the quality of US health care in the 1980s and 1990s, and is author or coauthor of more than 20 consumer-health books. He is also a featured columnist in *Bottom Line/Health*, *www.BottomLineHealth.com*.

REPORT #8

Sell Your Home and See the World!

How would you like to make the world your retirement home? Lynne and Tim Martin did just that. Two years ago, they sold

*Prices subject to change.

their home in California, and they have been traveling the world ever since. *The Martins' advice...*

Making the Money Work

Our financial manager sends us $6,000 per month generated by our investments, but we also have Social Security and a small pension. People certainly could live on less than we do. Accommodations are a good place to cut back—the cost of rentals overseas varies considerably with size, season, location and amenities.

● **Housing.** Most tourists stay in pricey hotels and visit areas for only a week or two. We rent furnished apartments and stay a minimum of one month in each location, usually longer. That greatly lowers our housing and travel costs and lets us get a far better feel for the area before we move on.

In California, our total housing expenses added up to around $3,600 a month, including the mortgage, home-maintenance bills, utility bills, homeowner's insurance, taxes and so forth. On the road, our rentals typically cost $1,500 to $2,500 per month and include utilities and Internet service.

Renting tips: We've had success using the rental-listing sites VRBO.com and HomeAway.com. These sites seem to do a good job vetting their property owners. *Also...*

● **Destinations.** We try not to spend too much time in pricey cities such as London and Paris. When we do visit an expensive location, we balance our budget by staying some place much more affordable next, such as Portugal, Mexico or Turkey. We often can keep our spending to $5,000 a month in such places.

● **Dining.** We try not to eat more than three or four meals per week in restaurants. Furnished rental apartments include kitchens, cookware, dishes and utensils, so we easily can cook for ourselves. One of the first things we do when we arrive in a new rental is find a nearby grocery store—the sooner we get groceries into the apartment, the lower our temptation to eat out.

● **Transportation within a country.** We usually choose properties near a public transit system. Monthly public transit passes are quite affordable in most cities, and there often is a senior discount.

● **Transportation to and from countries.** We take planes and trains and, when it's practical, rent cars. We buy almost everything with a credit card to rack up mileage points.

We also use repositioning cruises. These are voyages that cruise lines schedule primarily to move a ship from one part of the world to another. They can be an economical and enjoyable way to travel between continents. You can find repositioning cruises listed on RepositioningCruises.com or on the cruise lines' own Web sites.

Living With Less Stuff

When we decided to travel full-time, we put some of our possessions in storage, gave some to our kids and got rid of the rest. One of our daughters receives the mail, which has dwindled to almost nothing.

We each have a 30-inch rolling duffel bag and a carry-on bag. We initially worried that living with limited possessions would be a challenge. In fact, it has been liberating and wonderful.

One thing we do travel with in abundance is electronics. We each have a laptop, a smartphone (which we usually only use in the US) and an ereader, which allows us to carry an entire library without much weight.

Health Matters

Health care can be a concern for full-time travelers. Living on the road means that you can't see your regular doctor when you're sick...and Medicare doesn't cover medical care obtained outside the US.

We pay around $400 a month for a high-deductible international insurance policy that provides coverage for foreign medical emergencies and will evacuate us back to the US for medical care if necessary. Companies offering policies such as these include Seven Corners (*www.SevenCorners.com*) and Allianz (*www.Allianz WorldwideCare.com*), among others.

In our experience, very good medical care is available around much of the world, and it often costs substantially less than in the US.

Lynne and Tim Martin, a retired couple who, for the past few years, have traveled the world without a fixed home. They run the Web site HomeFreeAdventures.com and Lynne is the author of *Home Sweet Anywhere*, a book about full-time travel in retirement (Sourcebooks).

How to Get Guaranteed Protection For Your Nest Egg

Get FDIC insurance for CDs worth as much as $20 million without having to open 80 separate accounts of $250,000 each—the maximum insured per account by the FDIC. Use the Certificate of Deposit Account Registry Service (CDARS) that is offered by a growing network of banks. Through CDARS, your money appears in a single account but it is actually spread out among multiple accounts by the bank, so that it's fully insured. CDARS rates often are higher than those for standard CDs.

Information: 866-776-6426, *www.cdars.com*.

Money, *www.time.com/money*

Retire Earlier and Richer Than You Thought

Retiring before you reach age 65 may be tempting—but it also can be risky. The primary reason is inflation. Even a modest increase in prices has a huge cumulative effect over time, and Americans today are living longer than ever. The federal government calculates that a 50-year-old American woman will live to an average age of 80…a man, to about 75. If prices rise by just 2% a year, your expenses will increase by nearly 50% in 20 years. At 4% inflation, they actually will more than double. A good way to determine your yearly lifestyle needs is to add up six months of your fixed expenses—including mortgage payments, income taxes, property taxes and insurance. Also look back six months in your checkbook and credit card statements for any expenses that may have been left out. Double the amount you spent during those six months to arrive at your yearly income need. *Here are case histories of some of my clients who wanted to retire early and were able to pull it off…*

Tom and Julia

Five years ago, Tom, then 58, worked as an auto mechanic. His wife, Julia, 57, worked at a department store. Together, they earned about $125,000 a year. Since both were unhappy with their jobs, they wanted to retire early. Neither had a pension, but they were conscientious savers and hoped that their $470,000 investment portfolio would generate enough income for them to live on.

Income need: $40,000 a year, including $7,500 for property and income taxes...$8,000 for two health insurance policies...and $24,500 (about $2,000 a month) for all other expenditures— food, home maintenance and repairs, entertainment, travel, utilities, car and homeowners insurance, etc.

Decision: I advised Tom and Julia against early retirement, but I urged them both to find more satisfying work. Their investment portfolio would have to grow by 8.5% a year in order to generate the necessary annual income of $40,000. A more realistic return assumption would be between 7% and 8% per year.

Retirees should never take so much out of their portfolios that they can't continue to grow and outpace inflation. Today, most retirees should invest in stocks and bonds that together earn an average of about 7% and should withdraw no more than 5% a year. The two-percentage-point differential will offset inflation. What if inflation were to exceed 2%? They would have to live on a smaller percentage of their assets or find additional sources of income. They rejected my suggestion that they consider selling their home and buy a less expensive one, but a high inflation rate could force them to rethink that decision. I advised Tom and Julia to continue working for five years. During that time, their portfolio would grow at about $35,000 a year. They could save another $25,000 per year from their salaries. In five years, their portfolio would reach approximately $770,000. At that point, they could consider retiring.

Today: At ages 63 and 62, respectively, Tom and Julia are retired and close to accessing their Social Security benefits, which would allow them to take less income from their savings. Perhaps they will be able to withdraw 4% to 5% from their portfolio instead of the 6% that they withdraw now.

Lesson: Don't overestimate your savings. Your nest egg of nearly $500,000 may sound impressive, but it won't go far if you stop working too soon or if you need considerable income from it.

Ron and Carol

Three years ago, Ron, then 54, made about $80,000 a year as a telecommunications engineer. His wife, Carol, then 53, sold real estate and earned $30,000 to $50,000 per year, depending on her commissions. Ron lost his job when his company downsized. Both Ron and Carol wanted to retire, but they were willing to consider having one of them continue working. Of course, for Ron to continue to work, he would have to find another job.

Income need: The couple calculated that they would need $40,000 a year for their retirement. Their income-producing assets included Carol's IRA, which was worth about $200,000. Ron and Carol decided against long-term-care insurance, which would have cost about $5,000 per year for both. Ron's pension fund could not be tapped for monthly income payments before age 65. Until then, the assets were available to him only in a lump-sum payout of $260,000.

Decision: I advised Carol to keep working and Ron to withdraw the $260,000 pension in a lump sum. He rolled it over to an IRA and began taking distributions. There is normally a 10% tax penalty on early withdrawals from IRAs, but Ron took advantage of Code Section 72(t), which allows IRA holders to avoid the penalty as long as withdrawals last for five years or until the age of 59½, whichever occurs later. Under a complex IRS formula, Ron was required to withdraw $23,000 per year, or 5% of their total nest egg of $460,000 ($200,000 + $260,000). Meanwhile, Ron and Carol's combined retirement assets could be expected to grow at about 7%. Since the $23,000 a year in income was short of the $40,000 that they needed, Carol would have to continue working fulltime to add to their capital.

Today: Their assets stand at about $600,000—the result of growth in the couple's $460,000 nest egg and additional annual investments by Carol. They hope to eventually build their nest egg up to $1 million, so that when Carol retires they can conservatively take $45,000 every year (4.5% a year) to supplement Social Security.

Lesson: Don't view retiring early as an all-or-nothing proposition. Continuing to work part-time—or having one spouse continue working full-time—often is a better option.

Bob and Maria

Bob and Maria, both 55, recently faced a decision that many must make these days. His employer, a computer company, offered him an early retirement package with a choice of starting pension benefits immediately or, to get a higher monthly benefit, waiting until he was 62. (She didn't earn any income.) The couple had to decide whether the early pension benefit—plus income from $550,000 worth of other assets—would be enough to maintain their lifestyle. Bob also needed $10,000 of seed capital to start his own part-time consulting business.

Income need: They estimated their total monthly expenses at $6,000, or $72,000 a year. The early pension benefit came to approximately $4,000 a month, versus $4,800 at age 62. There was no provision in the pension plan for a lump-sum payout.

Decision: Despite the prospect of a higher pension benefit at age 62, I advised Bob to begin drawing benefits immediately, at age 55. Doing so would enable him and Maria to retire early and Bob to launch his second career part-time. The additional $2,000 a month needed to maintain their lifestyle would come from their $550,000 investment portfolio, at a withdrawal rate of approximately 4.5% per year.

Reason: If Bob waited until age 62 to start taking his pension benefits, he would receive only $800 more a month, but over the intervening seven years, he would forgo $336,000—based on $4,000 a month. Moreover, the couple's $550,000 in other assets wouldn't produce enough to live on, allow Bob to start his consulting business and cover inflation. Another factor in Maria and Bob's decision—whether his pension's survivorship benefit would be adequate to support Maria if she were to outlive him. She would receive $2,400 a month, assuming Bob waited until age 62 to take benefits. (Payments would be $2,000 if he started to take benefits before age 62.) Since the pension would not provide adequately for her, I suggested that Bob purchase life insurance. A male nonsmoker pays about $500 a month for a $500,000 policy at age 55. Bob would have to withdraw this money from his portfolio. Fortunately, he had the resources to do this. Purchasing insurance also can be a worthwhile strategy for couples who don't have pensions. For easy comparison shopping, you can find free life insurance quotes at *www.insure.com* or *www.accuquote.com*.

Lesson: It is not always best to put off taking pension or Social Security benefits to get a higher payout in the future. Make sure you do the math before you decide.

Robert J. Reby, CFP, president, Reby Advisors, a firm which advises clients on how to preserve and increase their wealth, Danbury, Connecticut.

REPORT #11

Free Benefits for Seniors

The Web site *www.benefitscheckup.org* is an online service that identifies more than 2,000 government and private benefit programs for those age 55 or over. Users fill out a confidential questionnaire and receive a personalized report listing programs and benefits they may be eligible to receive, along with detailed descriptions of programs and contact information.

The National Council on Aging, 251 18th St. S., Arlington, Virginia 22202.

REPORT #12

The Instant Pension Plan

In the past, retirees could rely on pensions and Social Security to replace most of their preretirement income. A 401(k) plan or IRA and personal savings provided additional support. Today, with fewer companies providing pension plans, nonpension resources often are the sole support. Unfortunately, 401(k)s do not guarantee a steady income stream.

To ensure that retirees will not outlive their savings, most need to create their own pensions...

How it works...

You can simulate your own pension plan by purchasing an immediate annuity. In exchange for your lump-sum payment, an insurance company agrees to provide a stable, guaranteed income every month for the remainder of your life. There is no right or wrong age at which you should purchase an immediate annuity.

Consider buying one when you need to replace or supplement your income. *Smart strategy...*

• **Ask whether your employer offers an annuity option via your retirement plan**—it may offer a more generous payout than an annuity you would purchase privately.

• **Compare annuity payout rates** and request free reports at *www.immediateannuities.com* (800-872-6684). There can be big differences among providers.

Also: Whether you're buying through your employer or on your own, make sure the company's claims-paying ability is rated A+ or better by A.M. Best (908-439-2200, *www.ambest.com*) or AA by Standard & Poor's (877-772-5436, *www.sandp.com*).

• **Factor in expenses.** Compare net results or monthly income amounts from different providers. *Annuity options...*

Your monthly annuity income depends on your age, the size of your lump-sum payment and any special features you choose. For instance, for a $100,000 straight life annuity purchased directly from a financial institution, a typical 65-year-old male could get about $557 a month. (Purchasing one via an employer might generate a higher payout.) Payments from a straight life annuity stop when you die, whether death occurs in the first year of the annuity or 30 years later. In the example above, the retiree would get $6,684 a year and so would have to live about 15 years to recover his initial investment without interest. *There are features you can add that adjust for these and other uncertainties...*

• **Life income for a fixed period.** If you die soon after the annuity payouts begin, your beneficiaries continue to receive payments for the period contracted—say, for 10 or 20 years. This feature will decrease the monthly payout—so, with a 20-year fixed period, the 65-year-old male in the example above and, subsequently, his beneficiaries, might receive a monthly payout of $515.

Who should choose this option: People who want expenses to be covered whether they are living or not, for an established period of time, possibly until other income sources kick in. This feature is not for people who want to ensure payment for the life of a coannuitant, such as a spouse.

• **Fixed period only.** This type of annuity pays income only for a specific length of time—for instance, exactly 10 years. This approach provides you with the highest monthly payout—for example, the 65-year-old male might receive a check for $910 every month for the 10 years.

Who should choose this option: Someone whose main concern is having income for a specific period and who knows that future income sources will be available after that period.

• **Cost-of-living rider.** If you're concerned that inflation will erode the value of your annuity payment over time, you may want to shop for a provider that will build in a cost-of-living adjustment. Some insurers allow you to increase your payout by, say, 3% each year. Others base increases on changes in the Consumer Price Index. Of course, this feature will mean a reduced monthly payout at first, depending on the extent of the increase or inflation protection, but you'll come out ahead if you live long enough.

Who should choose this option: People who don't think they can hedge against inflation in less costly ways—for instance, by combining an immediate annuity with equity investments. Such a strategy can hedge against inflation effectively while maximizing current income.

• **Joint-and-survivor.** This annuity continues paying a percentage of income—typically, 50% to 100%—to your spouse or beneficiary after your death. The higher the percentage earmarked for your beneficiary and the younger he/she is, the smaller the monthly payout.

Important: Seek advice from a fee-only consultant (not a commissioned salesperson) to determine the best approach. For instance, purchasing a life insurance policy along with an immediate annuity may be more tax efficient for your situation than a joint-and-survivor annuity. Many of the above features can be combined, so it's critical to compare apples to apples when choosing an annuity.

When to Buy

Given today's lower interest rates, you might be concerned that now is not the best time to purchase an annuity. It's true that potentially higher interest rates in the future may mean a higher annuity payout if you wait, but in the meantime, you might earn less on your cash than required to meet all your needs. If your income need is immediate but you are concerned about the level of interest rates, consider dollar cost averaging annuity purchases over the next two to three years and/or purchasing some inflation protection.

Best strategy: Consider buying an annuity now with some of your money to cover your fixed cash needs. Then invest the remainder of your savings for the longer term. You may rest more comfortably investing in stocks or other securities knowing that your fixed expenses will be covered. Don't forget to set aside some cash for emergencies and, if you wish, for your heirs. Keep in mind that annuities aren't for everyone. If you can live comfortably on the income from your investments without worrying about exhausting your principal, then an annuity may not be appropriate. Seek the counsel of a trusted adviser to set up a retirement income strategy.

Stacy L. Schaus, CFP, executive vice president and leader of the defined contribution practice at PIMCO, Newport Beach, California.

REPORT #13

How Not to Get Shortchanged By Social Security

I s the government calculating your Social Security benefits correctly? If it isn't, you may not get the amount to which you are entitled once you retire. If you have already retired, you may not be receiving as large a monthly check as you should. *How to prevent mistakes and how to correct them if they do occur...*

Mistake: Faulty earnings data.

Social Security benefits are based on your 35 highest-earning years, as reported to the government by your employers. If an employer has given the government incorrect salary data or if the government has erred in recording the information it received, you may miss out on full benefits. A $100 mistake early in your career is not likely to have much impact on benefits, but a $10,000 error made during a peak-salary year could lower benefits by several hundred dollars a year.

What to do: Look at your Social Security Administration (SSA) statement that the government sends to you each year around your birthday. For each year of employment, the statement lists the earnings on which Social Security taxes were based. It also estimates your benefits if you retire at the earliest age of eligibility (62) or if you wait for full benefits. Compare earnings listed in the SSA statement with income listed on W-2 forms in your tax records. If you spot a discrepancy, call the nationwide number (800-772-1213) to contact your local SSA. Most corrections can be made by phone. You also can use this number to request a statement. It helps to have your W-2 (or tax returns if you are selfemployed) for the incorrect years. If you don't, the SSA can use your employment information to search its records and correct the mistake. If the SSA can't find your records, contact your employer for the year in question to obtain a copy of your W-2.

Once your earnings data are corrected, the SSA will send you a confirming notice. If you don't receive one in three to four months, contact the SSA again. It is best to make an appointment with a staff member, but it is also possible to handle problems by phone. Regardless of how you communicate, ask the staffer for a direct phone number so you can easily get back in touch. Then double-check the correction by making sure it appears on the following year's SSA statement. If the SSA fails to make this or any other type of correction, start the appeals process by writing a letter within 60 days (plus five days after the postmark for mailing time) of the date of the SSA decision notice. It also is wise to contact your US representative. Many members of Congress have staffers who help constituents in their dealings with the SSA. As a last resort, hire an attorney with experience in Social Security matters. To research attorneys, go to *www.lawyers.com*.

Mistake: Faulty calculations.

Even when it has the correct earnings data, the SSA occasionally errs in calculating benefits. It is wise to suspect a miscalculation if you have already discovered other errors in your annual statement.

What to do: Tell the SSA about your misgivings, and ask that your benefits be recalculated. If you do still have doubts, you can make the calculation yourself by using the SSA's formula, which is now available on its Web site. Log on to *www. socialsecurity.gov*.

Since this math is complex, consider asking a knowledgeable accountant to do the calculation or ask your employer's human resources department for assistance. If you find an error, point it out to the SSA in the same way that you would notify it of a mistake in your earnings data. Make sure you receive a confirming letter and that the correction appears on next year's statement. If you are already receiving benefits, the SSA will reimburse you for the amount of the error.

Mistake: Incorrect address.

If the SSA doesn't have your correct address, your earnings may not be recorded. You also may miss important correspondence. You should suspect a problem if you fail to receive an annual statement. Even if you do receive a yearly statement, make sure that the address includes your exact street number and zip code.

What to do: If there is a mistake in your address, contact the IRS—the SSA depends on the IRS for addresses. To make your correction, ask for IRS Form 8822, Change of Address. (You can request the form by calling 800-829-3676 or download it from the IRS Web site at *www.irs.gov*.)

Mistake: Wrong personal data.

Benefits are in jeopardy if your name or date of birth in SSA records isn't the same as it appears in IRS files. Mistakes often occur after a marriage or divorce. When women marry, for example, their employers routinely start reporting their earnings under their married names. The Social Security records, however, still may be listed under their maiden names. This can result in lower benefits.

What to do: Whenever you change your name, ask the SSA for Form SS-5, Application for a Social Security Card, and then submit it with the correct information. The form can be downloaded from the SSA Web site. If you suspect that you have forgotten to notify the SSA of a name change earlier in your career, review the earnings data on your annual SSA statement for the years immediately following a marriage or divorce. The earnings should match the amounts on your W-2 forms for the same years. Though less frequent, mistakes occur with dates of birth. If IRS and SSA records don't match, your full earnings may not be reported. Benefits can be delayed if SSA records show the date of birth is later than it actually is. Use Form SS-5 to correct this type of mistake.

Mistake: Missing benefits from a spouse.

Check for errors in your spouse's Social Security account as well as your own.

Reason: If you outlive your spouse, you are entitled to a portion of his/her benefits, depending on your age.

What to do: If your spouse is deceased and you suspect a mistake in the benefits you are receiving, check the accuracy of your spouse's last annual statement. If you do not have it, ask the SSA to send you one. (You may be asked for a copy of your marriage certificate.)

If you believe that the error lies in calculating the proportion of your spouse's benefits that you're receiving, phone the SSA to verify the amount, or go to the Web site *www.socialsecurity.gov/sur vivorplan/ifyou5.htm*. The site includes a table for determining the proportion of benefits to which surviving spouses are entitled.

Often-overlooked benefit: At full retirement age, you maybe entitled to as much as 50% of benefits from a former spouse who is age 62 or older, even if the spouse has not applied for Social Security benefits. (You must be unmarried, and your former marriage must have lasted at least 10 years.)

What to do: For an estimate of what you're entitled to receive from a former spouse's earnings record, call the SSA.

Donna A. Clements, manager of Social Security Information Services for Mercer Human Resource Consulting, which helps some of the country's best known companies solve Social Security and other benefits problems, Louisville, Kentucky, *www. imercer.com.*

REPORT #14

Social Security Tips and Traps

Every day, more Americans discover the Social Security safety net they rely on is filled with complex traps that can reduce their potential benefits by tens of thousands of dollars.

One of the complications: For married couples, Social Security rules and strategies can be very different from what they are for people who are single, widowed or divorced.

Below we explain ways to avoid some of the most common, confusing and potentially costly traps for married couples and explore a quandary that affects all kinds of retirees—when to start collecting benefits.

Trap #1: **Many men think that they should start receiving benefits as soon as they are eligible because men have shorter life spans, on average, than women.** Monthly benefit checks increase in size for every month that you delay retirement from age 62 to 70. But many men assume that it's sensible to start benefits as soon as they retire because longevity tables (and in some cases, family history and/or their own health) indicate that they're unlikely to live far into their 80s. And Social Security calculators often suggest that delaying benefits is a money loser if you die before age 80.

While that logic can be sound for single men, it tends to be a mistake for husbands—particularly husbands who significantly outearned their wives during their careers and are older than their wives and/or have healthy wives from long-lived families.

Better strategy: Generally, higher-earning husbands should base decisions about whether to take benefits early on the longer of the two spouses' projected life spans, which usually is the wife's. That's because after a man in this situation dies, his widow is entitled to a survivor benefit equal to the benefit that the husband had been receiving. (However, this survivor benefit would be reduced if the widow began receiving it prior to her so-called "standard" or "full" retirement age. That age varies according to what year you were born and may be slightly different for widows/widowers.)

Once this survivor benefit is taken into account, many households would be better off if the husband delays starting his benefits as long as possible up to age 70—even if that means he doesn't receive much from Social Security before he dies. (This also could apply to wives who significantly outearned younger husbands, but because women tend to have longer life spans, benefit calculators are less likely to suggest that women should claim their benefits early.)

Example: Mr. Jones, who is 66 (his standard retirement age) starts collecting $2,000 per month. If he lives 16 more years—a typical life span for a 66-year-old man—he will have received a total of $384,000* from Social Security. Waiting until age 70 to start benefits might reduce the total benefits he receives—his monthly checks would increase to $2,640, but the loss of four years' worth of checks means that his take would be just over $380,000, which is nearly $4,000 less than if he had started collecting at age 66.

*Estimates of future Social Security income provided in this article do not include future inflation adjustments.

But if Mr. Jones is married, for instance to a healthy woman four years his junior, then delaying benefits until age 70 might pay off better. In that case, after Mr. Jones dies, Mrs. Jones continues to receive $2,640 per month in survivor benefits, rather than the $2,000 she would have received had Mr. Jones started his benefits at age 66. If she lives a typical woman's life span—in this case, staying alive for seven years after her husband's death—she would receive $53,760 extra from Social Security, offsetting her husband's $4,000 loss many times over.

Social Security Traps for Singles, Widows and Widowers

Some of the traps that ensnare current and future Social Security recipients apply especially to people who are single or widowed...

Trap for Singles

Trap #2: **Bad timing.** If you're single, there are certain ages when it is most advantageous to wait a little longer to start receiving benefits. That's because your monthly benefit amount increases in size for every month that you delay starting Social Security from age 62 to 70—but it doesn't increase at a consistent pace throughout those years.**

For instance, if you start your benefits at age 66, or whatever your so-called "standard" or "full" retirement age is, you probably are doing so exactly at the moment when continuing to postpone the start offers the greatest rewards—even though it's the age that the Social Security Administration (SSA) considers the "normal" time to retire.

When you crunch the numbers, it turns out that there actually are two windows during which it is especially inopportune for most single people to claim benefits if they wish to maximize the total amount they receive. One window runs from age 62 and one month through age 63 and 11 months...while the other is centered around your standard retirement age—age 65 and five months through age 66 and seven months if your standard retirement age is 66.

**To calculate the amounts you could get at each age, go to *www.SSA.gov/oact/quick calc/index.html*. Decisions about when to start Social Security also depend on life expectancy (go to *www.SSA.gov/oact/population/longevity.html* for a guide to life-expectancy calculations) and on whether you still are earning substantial employment income, which could mean much of your Social Security benefits would be lost to taxes.

If your standard retirement age is higher than 66, the windows during which it's best not to start benefits are within eight months before or after your standard retirement age and within approximately 12 months before or after the date that is three years prior to your standard retirement age.

Example: If your standard retirement age is 67, the windows to avoid are between 66 and four months and 67 and eight months… and between approximately age 63 and age 65.

All this is true for married people, too, but married people have additional benefits options, such as spousal benefits, that mean starting benefits at standard retirement age sometimes makes sense.

Trap for Widows and Widowers

Trap #3: **Permanently choosing between survivor benefits and your own retirement benefits.** The best option usually isn't one or the other—it's one and then the other. Many widows and widowers depend on their Social Security checks to pay the bills. Yet most receive less from the Social Security system than they should because of this simple trap.

When widows and widowers explore their benefit options, they typically are told that they must choose between claiming a benefit based on their own earnings and claiming survivor benefits based on their departed spouse's earnings—not both. The vast majority select whichever of these is larger and then receive that amount each month for the rest of their lives. These checks often are relatively small because survivors tend to start their benefits as soon as they're eligible—some don't have any other way to pay the bills.

Widows and widowers are allowed to start their survivor benefits as early as age 60, but the sooner they claim them, the lower their monthly checks will be. Start benefits at age 60, and you will receive just 71.5% of the amount you would receive if you start benefits at your standard retirement age (assuming that is age 66).

What most widows and widowers don't realize is that while they can't receive both their retirement benefit and their survivor benefit at the same time, they can—and, in most cases, should—eventually switch from one to the other. This switching strategy can produce tens of thousands of dollars in additional benefits, particularly when both spouses had significant earnings during their working lives.

Example: A woman is widowed at age 62. She has a standard retirement benefit of $1,657 and a standard survivor benefit of $2,245. In this situation, most widows simply would take the survivor benefit and receive $1,862 per month for life (that's the $2,245 survivor benefit minus a reduction for starting benefits at 62, four years prior to standard retirement age). If this woman lives to age 85, she will receive a total of $506,464 from the Social Security system.

Much better: If this woman instead claimed her own retirement benefit at age 62, she would receive $1,277 per month ($1,657 minus the reduction for starting four years before standard retirement age) until age 66...at which point she could switch to her standard $2,245 survivor benefit. This strategy would produce additional benefits of more than $62,000 if she lives past age 85.

Trap #4: **Your standard retirement age for survivor benefits might be different from your standard retirement age for retiree benefits.** The SSA is slowly phasing in a higher standard retirement age. If you were born in 1937 or earlier, you can retire at age 65 and receive your standard retirement benefit. But if you were born after 1937, your standard retirement age falls somewhere between age 65 and two months and age 67, depending on the year of your birth.

What most people don't realize: The SSA is using a slightly different schedule to increase the standard retirement age for survivor benefits. This could cause widows and widowers to accidentally delay the start of survivor benefits beyond their survivor benefits standard retirement age, costing them some monthly checks without increasing the size of future checks. (Those born between 1945 and 1956 are not affected—for them, both standard retirement ages are 66.)

To find your survivor standard retirement age: Go to *www.SSA. gov/survivorplan/survivorchartred.htm*.

Example: If you were born in 1956, your standard retirement age for retiree benefits is 66 and four months—but your standard retirement age for survivor benefits is exactly 66.

William Meyer, founder and managing principal of Social Security Solutions, Inc., which provides personalized Social Security benefits optimization strategies, Leawood, Kansas. He previously served in executive roles at H&R Block and Charles Schwab & Co. *www.SocialSecuritySolutions.com*

How to Write Your Life Story!

Everyone has unique life experiences that he or she should preserve for future generations. Writing your autobiography is the perfect way to tell your story and pass on valuable life lessons.

1. Research

Before you start to write a single word, be sure to have all of your facts in hand...

• **Remember.** Buy yourself a stack of index cards and begin remembering the times of your life. Record a single event on each index card in a single sentence or phrase. Add the date if you can remember that. Do this for all the events you think you would like to include in the book. Keep a binder, index cards or a tape recorder handy at all times to document recollections.

• **Gather information.** Talk with friends and relatives about times past, look through old photo albums, review old record books in your church library or town hall and go to the library to access facts and figures. Some communities have societies dedicated to local history and genealogy. Check out your *Yellow Pages* or local library to find one in your area. The Church of Jesus Christ of Latter-day Saints (Mormon) also has genealogical resources available to the public at their local Family History Centers. Check their Web site at *www.familysearch.org*.

2. Organize

After you've gathered your information, organize it...

• **Create a time line.** Organize all your material by milestones—graduations, weddings, births, job changes. On a sheet of paper, draw a horizontal line. Starting from the left, fill in when you were born and then, moving to the right, fill in when you started school, etc.

• **Arrange the facts.** Create an outline for your story by using one (or a combination) of two ways to organize...

 • **Chronological—proceed in sequence.** Each chapter of your life can be grouped in 10-year periods.

 • **By subject—group reminiscences into categories, such as education, romance, raising children, career, travel, etc.** Each topic can then be handled chronologically. Keep the reader in mind. Make sure the events flow logically from one to the other.

3. Write

Use a computer, if you can, to set your story down. It will check your spelling and grammar. It also has features that allow you to easily refine your draft. *Keep the autobiography interesting by asking yourself key questions as you write...*

- **Does this incident tell the reader something important about my life?**
- **Will this episode move the book along or bog it down?**
- **Must I include every person I ever met or every event in my life?** To bring the scenes to life, write in the first person so that the story has your voice. Set the mood by using one or more of the five senses in each scene you describe.

4. Edit

After you have finished writing, put the project aside for a while. You need to be detached and objective about the story when editing it. You may need to edit your manuscript several times before it reads well. Use grammar and style reference books—a good dictionary usually will provide all the guidance you require in terms of spelling and punctuation. *Merriam-Webster's Collegiate Dictionary* includes "A Handbook of Style" among its sections. And all writers can benefit from *Roget's International Thesaurus*.

5. Publish

Once you have written your story, consider publishing your book using print-on-demand (POD) technology, available from POD self-publishing companies. WordWright.biz (*www.word wright.biz*), specializes in helping new authors write, publish and distribute their stories. Memoirs can take a variety of forms—from poetry to prose. They can publish as few as 25 copies for family and friends.

Joan R. Neubauer, author of several books, including *From Memories to Manuscript: The Five-Step Method of Writing Your Life Story* (Ancestry) and *The Complete Idiot's Guide to Journaling* (Alpha). Based in Alpine, Texas, she also teaches classes and conducts workshops on a wide variety of topics, from writing to business.

Don't Act Your Age

Older adults who imagine themselves as 20 years younger and who think, act and speak as they did two decades earlier have better memory and manual dexterity than people of similar ages who act as old as they really are. The ones who act young look younger than their real ages, too, although not a full 20 years younger.

Bottom line: Positive expectations and beliefs about aging make people healthier and more vital.

Ellen J. Langer, PhD, professor, psychology department, Harvard University.

Top Retirement Regrets: Many You Can Still Fix

Enjoying retirement is near the top of most people's wish lists. But when I was researching a book on retirement, I heard from retirees what they wished they had done differently before retiring—and many of these retirees had the same regrets.

By heeding the advice of the already-retired, you can avoid the common regrets and enjoy your retirement that much more...

• **Not retiring sooner** (because maybe you can afford to do so). Most of the retirees I spoke with were enjoying their retirement immensely, and when I asked about any regrets, they often said, "My only regret is that I should have retired sooner!" Many went on to explain that once they settled into retirement, they found that their spending and general cost of living dropped to a level where they realistically could have afforded to retire earlier...with the notable exception of health care.

• **Not doing your homework.** Many retirees admitted that they took the time to learn how some of the most basic features of retirement worked only when they were on the cusp of retirement or even after they were fully retired. Many retirees confessed that they waited too long to learn the ins and outs of Social Security and Medicare...what benefits they were entitled to receive under their pensions and retirement accounts...and the fine points of things such as long-term-care insurance and reverse mortgages.

Not doing this type of homework earlier cost one person I interviewed $6,000 a year in lost pension benefits that she could have started collecting years earlier, while she still was working. She told me, "I looked into it only when I was actually ready to stop working—a big mistake."

- **Not burying the hatchet sooner.** It's never too early to patch things up with family members or others with whom you have a strained relationship, but carrying that emotional baggage with you into retirement can tarnish your later years. Not only will you have more time in retirement to sit around and brood about such unpleasant affairs (if that's how you choose to spend your time), but having close, supportive relationships with family and friends—a care network that you can depend on—can be a tremendous asset, particularly in retirement.

- **Not planning for all that leisure time.** If you are used to working full time and have few leisure-time interests, filling all that newfound time during retirement can be a real challenge. Retirees say that you should cultivate hobbies and other activities before you retire so that you're not overwhelmed by all of that additional free time. Also, if one spouse is used to being alone around the house and has been primarily responsible for managing the household, injecting a second person into that situation can create stress. Respect each other's boundaries and need for alone time (and agree upon shared household responsibilities) *before* you retire for an easier transition.

- **Not downsizing earlier.** Downsizing your household and lifestyle—by doing such things as moving to a smaller home, getting rid of unwanted items and maybe selling off a second car—is a pretty common practice among retired folks. And once they've done it, many retirees say they wished they had done it years earlier, long before they retired. Of course, downsizing earlier also can allow you to build your retirement nest egg that much faster and allow you to retire with less debt—or better yet, with no debt.

- **Not kicking a bad habit earlier.** Having more time on your hands can prompt you to further indulge in any bad habits. Maybe the cocktail hour you have always enjoyed starts earlier in the day and lasts longer…or an occasional trip to the racetrack becomes a daily gambling obsession. Being relatively isolated at home and having more free time to indulge are among the chief reasons why substance abuse among elderly people is a growing problem, according to a recent study by the Substance Abuse and Mental Health Services Administration.

• **Not traveling earlier in retirement.** Many older retirees expressed regrets about not traveling or pursuing other activities that require more physical stamina at the front end of their retirement years. There is a tendency to postpone those activities when you're newly retired, both because you believe that your health will remain largely the same and you fear burning through too much of your retirement savings too soon. "Do what you can when you still can," one globe-trotting retiree told me, "because you never know how much longer you'll be able to do it."

• **Not taking better care of your health.** Entering retirement in ill health can have dire consequences in terms of both quality of life and finances. Maintaining optimum health throughout life and specifically "going into training" leading up to retirement, as one retiree put it, truly can make your retirement the best years of your life. But don't despair if your health is less than perfect when you hit retirement. A number of retirees said they were able to markedly improve their health once retired, when they had more time to devote to fitness.

Jeff Yeager is AARP's official "Savings Expert" and host of a weekly AARP web show on YouTube (YouTube.com/user/CheapLifeChannel). Based in Accokeek, Maryland, he is author of four popular books about frugal living, including his most recent, *How to Retire the Cheapskate Way* (Three Rivers). UltimateCheapskate.com

3

Travel and Entertainment Secrets

3 Ways to Save on...Cruises... Hotel Rates...Last-Minute Travel

Cruises

With nightly rates dropping to as little as $60 per person,* booking an economical cruise would seem to be as simple as stuffing yourself at the onboard dinner buffet. But many cruisers, initially pulled in by low fares, end up spending far more than expected on "extras." *The following three tips can keep your cruising budget afloat...*

1. Compare sellers. Though the base price for cruising won't change that much, those travel agencies that sell a number of cruises are rewarded by the cruise lines with extra perks for their customers. Shop around and see which sellers will be willing to "gift" you with free cabin upgrades, onboard ship credits (of $100 to $200), a waiving of gratuities and more. Start with large companies such as CruisesOnly.com...VacationsToGo.com...and Cruises.com.

2. Cruise on the fringe. Choose the sailings that occur on the fringes of the regular season, say, Alaska or the Mediterranean in May or September...or the Caribbean during hurricane season.

*Prices subject to change.

That last suggestion isn't as crazy as it sounds—the chances of being in the Caribbean during a storm are quite low.

3. Book your own excursions. On average, vacationers spend an additional 25% of the cost of the cruise once on board the ship and up to 75% more if they frequent the spa or casino! So set a budget, and stick to it. Shore excursions are the priciest onboard purchases, so book your own in advance through such companies as CruisingExcursions.com or Viator.com.

Hotel Rates

Hotel prices can change by the day, even by the hour. *But you can game the system somewhat by using the right Web sites…*

1. Air-hotel package Web sites. "Bundling" airfare and hotel can offer significant savings. That's because travel sellers can "hide" the hotel price within a package so that it's not so obvious how deeply the room rate has been slashed. For Europe, try Gate1Travel.com…Go-Today.com…and BMIT.com. Within the US, look at SouthwestVacations.com and the big sites such as Expedia, Travelocity and Orbitz. Expedia also is good for tropical destinations such as Hawaii and the Caribbean. Compare its offerings with those from VacMart.com…BookIt.com…and PleasantHolidays.com.

2. GetaRoom.com. The thinking here is that some prices are too good to be shown on the Internet. So this company encourages users to call its 800 number (800-468-3578) to get the most deeply slashed rates. Sometimes it works, sometimes not, but it doesn't cost anything to try.

3. Tingo.com. If you book a "Money Back" hotel room through Tingo, it promises to keep checking the rate for price changes. If the rate drops, it automatically refunds you the difference.

Example: One user was recently refunded $153 on a Paris hotel. It works very well on pricey properties, but on midrange and budget hotels, Tingo often doesn't have the lowest rates to begin with. You might do better at a more budget-oriented site, such as Hipmunk.com or Booking.com.

Last-Minute Travel…

Sometimes it pays to procrastinate. *You can get some great last-minute travel deals…*

1. Follow the deals. Never considered Iceland, but the price is superb? Why not! Three days in Vegas for a song? Doesn't matter that you don't gamble, really! For cruises leaving within 90 days, try *www.VacationsToGo.com*. Air/hotel packages at the last minute can be found through all the major companies (Priceline, Expedia, etc.), as well as specialists such as LastMinute.com.

2. Get Tweet bargains. Twitter has become the best source for last-minute airfares. Instead of losing a hefty commission fee to third-party Web sites (such as Orbitz or Travelocity), the airlines post "flash sales" on Twitter to move unsold seats through their own Web sites. The most prominent tweeter is @JetBlueCheeps, which posts sales for the coming weekend. @VirginAmerica and @AllegiantAir also are excellent sources, though even biggies such as American Airlines and Delta will tweet flash sales occasionally.

3. Go for this app. One hotel app (available for smartphones and tablets) tends to beat the pants off the competition. Called Hotel Tonight, it can be used only starting at noon on the day of travel and for 55 American cities (plus a handful in Canada, the UK, Holland and Ireland). It finds the cheapest rates three out of four times (at some very cushy properties), prices that are as much as 70% off the lowest rate.

Example: A $249 room at a Houston hotel recently went for $99, for a savings of $150.

Pauline Frommer, a nationally syndicated newspaper columnist and radio talk show host. She is a member of the Frommer guidebook family and a two-time winner of the North American Travel Journalists Association's Guidebook of the Year award. *www.Frommers.com/pauline*

REPORT #16

Travel Bargains You Didn't Know Existed...

How to Get a Hotel Room Upgraded Free

Look up a specific high-end room prior to checking in, and then ask to be upgraded to that room by name, such as the honeymoon suite. Make the front desk clerk's job easier by being specific about the type of room you want, such as one with a pool view, instead of just asking for a better room. If there are problems with your room, ask to be upgraded because of the inconvenience. If it's a special occasion such as a birthday or anniversary, be sure to tell the front desk clerk.

Men's Health. *www.MensHealth.com*

Fly in Luxury for the Price of Economy

You may be able to fly on a private jet for the cost of a commercial first-class or business-class ticket. London-based charter broker Air Partner (*www.EmptySectors.com*) helps fill seats when planes fly back to base or are between jobs. JetSuite, in California (*www.JetSuite.com*), offers SuiteDeals, which lets customers charter a four-passenger aircraft at huge last-minute savings (click on Daily Deals). Corporate Flight Management (615-220-1761), a collective-buying company in Tennessee, uses social networking to help charter companies fill seats.

The New York Times, *www.nytimes.com*

How to Fly for Free

Airlines typically give passengers bumped from flights vouchers for $200 to $800, so it may pay to be bumped.

If your schedule is flexible and you want to increase your odds of being bumped: Travel at peak times…book as many connections as possible to raise the chance of being bumped somewhere along the line…check the seat map before booking so you can choose a flight that is almost full…arrive at the gate early and tell the person at the check-in counter that you are available to be bumped…and take only a carry-on bag so your luggage does not have to be pulled from the plane.

Helpful: Voucher amounts often can be negotiated.

Scott Ford, a traveler who used vouchers to visit 400 cities in one year after being laid off and unable to find a job, quoted online at *DailyFinance.com*.

How to Get VIP Service All the Time

A nyone can get a last-minute reservation at a popular restaurant that is booked solid—if you know what to say and how to tip. *Here's what to do when you call at the last minute and are told no tables are available...*

- **Ask to speak with the maitre d'.** Get his or her name before your call is transferred.
- **When the maitre d' picks up, address him by his first name, and give your own full name.** That creates the impression that you have been to the restaurant before and know him.
- **Give your name, and say with empathy, "I know how busy you are tonight.** But if you could find a way to have a table for me at 8 pm, I would be happy to take care of you the right way." This language may feel uncomfortable or cagey, but it is the language that service professionals recognize.

  Helpful: Never mention a dollar figure—it is offensive and demeans his craft. Be specific with what you want. Otherwise you could end up eating at 5 pm or midnight.
- **If the answer is still no, take one last shot.** Say, "I don't mind waiting in the bar for a bit if it would help you out." Your flexibility lets him know that you are experienced and not unreasonable.
- **If you get a table, tip the maitre d' discreetly (no one should ever see).** Give him the folded bill(s) in your handshake. The tip amount depends on the caliber of the restaurant, how badly you want to get in and how hard the maitre d' had to work to get you the table—$10 is enough for a good restaurant on a typical night...$20 to $50 for more extreme circumstances, such as conventions, holidays, etc.

Valet Parking: Keeping Your Car Up Front...

When your waiter hands over your check, hand him/her your valet ticket stub, and ask him to give it to the valet, so that your car is waiting up front by the time you pay the bill and leave the restaurant.

Mark Brenner, author of *Tipping for Success! Secrets for How to Get In and Get Great Service* (Brenmark House) and founder of Brenmark House, a marketing solutions think tank for companies that require branding, marketing, sales and advertising strategies, Sherman Oaks, California.

America's 7 Natural Wonders

There are sights in America so breathtaking, destinations so inspiring, that those who see them remember the experiences for the rest of their lives. In a country as diverse and remarkable as the United States, the list of unforgettable places is almost endless. *But a few spots truly stand out…*

Denali National Park, Alaska

The six-million-plus-acre preserve features Mount McKinley, the highest peak on the continent, plus remarkable wildlife like moose, caribou, elk and grizzly bear. Visit between late May and September, when the weather is best. The entry fee is $10 per individual…(National Park Service, 907-683-2294, *www.nps.gov/dena*). Camp Denali offers a cluster of 18 rustic yet comfortable cabins in the park. This is the best way to experience Denali. In addition to gourmet food, you'll have access to the camp's guides and naturalists, who lead backcountry tours and give talks. (907-683- 2290, *www.campdenali.com*). For a more affordable visit, stay at one of the hotels that is clustered around the park's entrance, such as the White Moose Lodge. $90 to $110* (800-481-1232, *www.whitemooselodge.com*).

Go to *www.travelalaska.com* for more options.

Check with the National Park Service for camping information, *www.nps.gov/dena*.

Canyon de Chelly National Monument, Arizona

The Grand Canyon is a stunning sight, but a memorable canyon experience of a different sort is the less crowded Canyon de Chelly (pronounced "shay") on Navajo Nation land in northeast Arizona, with a gateway entrance in Chinle. Unlike the Grand Canyon, it features clay and stone Native American dwellings that are more than 1,000 years old. Navajo guides help you to explore and understand what you see. There is no fee to enter the park and to hike the White House Trail or drive the North and South Rim

*All lodging prices are per room per night double-occupancy, unless otherwise noted.

Drives (928-674-5500, *www.nps.gov/*). Access to the canyon floor is restricted.

The simple, no-frills Sacred Canyon Lodge, with its predominantly Navajo staff, is the only hotel within the park. Contact the lodge for prices (800-679-2473, *www.sacredcanyonlodge.com*).

Pacific Coast Highway, California

The Pacific Coast Highway (Route 1) is the greatest drive in America. It winds though idyllic California towns, past grand mansions and along some of the most stunning coastline in the world. The most impressive stretch is from Santa Monica, just north of Los Angeles, up to Sonoma County, north of San Francisco. Worthwhile visits along the way include Hearst Castle at $25 per adult (800-444-4445, *www.hearstcastle.org*)…picturesque Carmel (*www.carmelcalifornia.com*)…and the beautiful Big Sur region (*www.bigsurcalifornia.org*).

Big Sur is a particularly lovely place to spend the night. If money is no object, stay at the luxurious Ventana Inn & Spa for about $450 and up (800-628-6500, *www.ventanainn.com*). Those with tighter budgets might consider Deetjen's Big Sur Inn, where a simple room with a shared bath can be had for as little as $105 (831-667-2377, *www.deetjens.com*).

Middle Fork of the Salmon River, Idaho

Depending on the season, rafting down the Salmon River can offer anything from thrilling rapids to a leisurely journey. It's best to visit in May or June if you're looking for thrills…September for calm currents and relaxing fly-fishing…July or August for something in between. Rocky Mountain River Tours has an impressive safety record and employs expert guides. Book at least six months in advance (208-345-2400, *www.rafttrips.com*).

Glacier National Park, Montana

This national park along the Canadian border is called Little Switzerland because of its glacier-carved terrain. There are hundreds of miles of hiking trails, or you can tour by car. Visit in summer to avoid snow. $25 (summer); $15 (winter) for a seven-day vehicle permit (406-888-7800, *www.nps.gov/glac*). Park-run lodging includes the Glacier Park Lodge Hotel, with incredible views, for $159 and up...and Prince of Wales Hotel, which has rooms starting at $199 (406-892-2525, *www.glacierparkinc.com*).

Gettysburg National Military Park and Cemetery, Pennsylvania

Walking around this Civil War battlefield where more than 50,000 men died is a moving experience. Monuments, gravestones and relics preserve the memory of the war. Visit from June to mid-August and enjoy ranger-led Battle Walks and evening campfire programs. Admission to the park is free (717-334-1124, *www.nps.gov/gett*).

The Farnsworth House Inn bed-and-breakfast dates to 1810 and housed Confederate sharpshooters—you still can find bullet holes in the building. Rates are from $145 to $225 (717-334-8838, *www.farnsworthhouseinn.com*).

Northeast Kingdom, Vermont

Orleans, Essex and Caledonia counties in northeastern Vermont make up the Northeast Kingdom, marked with covered bridges, steepled churches and charming towns. In the fall, when the leaves change color, roads are packed with "leaf-peepers," so expect to move slowly (800-639-6379, *www.nekchamber.com*).

Patricia Schultz, New York City–based author of *1,000 Places to See Before You Die* and *1,000 Places to See in the USA and Canada Before You Die* (both from Workman).

REPORT #19

Free Vacation Villa and Luxury Car

Looking for a less expensive vacation? Consider exchanging homes. This type of service is provided in California, New York, Paris, London and other locations.

Advantages: You eliminate hotel expenses and, often, car-rental fees—a car sometimes comes with the house—and save money on eating out.

To find a home exchange: Post your own ad and answer ads for a fee on home-exchange Web sites, such as *www.homeexchange.com...www.digsville.com.*

Before exchanging: Build trust with your exchange partner with lots of pretrip communication...mention any concerns up front—if, for example, you don't permit any smoking in your home. All exchange partners should sign a written agreement and—for final assurance of commitment—exchange copies of their airline tickets. Exchangers who stay in your home for up to 30 days are considered guests and should be covered by your homeowner's insurance—verify this with your insurer. For any periods that are longer than 30 days, ask your insurance company about additional coverage.

Roy Prince, founder of HomeExchange.com, featuring listings in 150 countries, Hermosa Beach, California.

Play the Slots and Win

J osephine Crawford didn't believe the casino employee when he told her that she had just won $10 million. Her bet on the Megabucks nickel slot had paid off. The odds are infinitesimal that you'll ever duplicate Ms. Crawford's success at the slots, but you can still have lots of fun. And who knows? You just might get as lucky as she was—especially if you know the inside tricks to playing slot machines. *What you need to know...*

The Odds

Casinos try to take your mind off the odds. They introduce a constant stream of new slot games and offer eye-catching jackpots, such as new cars displayed on turntables in full view of the machines. Regardless of the enticements, the majority of slot machines give an edge of 1% to 10% to the house, a term used for the owner of the machine, whether it's a casino or a convenience store in Nevada. This means that most slot players "win" back only 90 cents to 99 cents of every dollar they play. These payback rates are calculated over the long run, which can be many thousands of games. So do not be misled when you see a player win several times during an hour's play at a particular machine. There eventually will be enough losses to bring the odds back in the house's favor. And you never know when those losses will occur. The more it costs to play a slot, the higher the payback rate usually is. Games that cost $5 or $10, for example, might pay back 99%, while a nickel game often returns no more than 90% and penny games pay even less.

Caution: Slot games on the Internet are becoming popular.

My advice: Stay away from all Internet slots. They're illegal to play in many US states, and there's no way of knowing what the payback rate is.

Also, keep in mind that even the best odds at slots aren't as good as the odds with other games, such as blackjack, that require skill, concentration and a good memory.

Improving Your Chances

The best slot machine odds are in Las Vegas—but not on the city's famous Strip. Casinos on the Strip—including Bally's, the Mirage and the Tropicana—do not need player-friendly slots because they enjoy a steady stream of tourists. The payback on 25-cent machines at Strip casinos is 93% or 94%, and on dollar games, it's 95% or 96%. Casinos off the Strip depend more on local residents who demand the incentive of better odds to play the slots. That's particularly true in the suburbs of Henderson and in North Las Vegas, where the payback at such casinos as Sunset Station, Fiesta Station and Green Valley Ranch is one or two percentage points higher than it is on the Strip.

In Atlantic City, the nickel slots usually have a payback rate of only 90%, while 91% or 92% is typical for quarter games and 94% for dollar slots. Casinos elsewhere in the country offer similar payback rates.

Today, video slots are popular, and they have the same payback rates as traditional mechanical machines, known as reel slots. Some of the worst paybacks are at Nevada's airports and convenience stores, where the payback rate can be as low as 75%. To find slots with the best payback rates, check one of the gaming publications that regularly report on them. Two magazines with monthly payback reports are *CasinoPlayer* and *StrictlySlots* (800-969-0711 or *www.strictlyslots.com*). In any one casino, all slots that cost the same usually have the same payback rate, regardless of the particular slot game that's featured on the machine.

Example: If you bet $1 in a Blazing 7s slot machine, you'll receive the same payback rate as you would by betting $1 in a machine that features Tabasco, another popular game. Nevertheless, many players really believe that some games are luckier than others. StrictlySlots regularly asks its readers to name the reel slot games where they experienced the most success. Their choices have been Double Diamond, Red White & Blue, Wheel of Fortune, Triple Diamond and Blazing 7s. Video slots considered the luckiest are Cleopatra, Jackpot Party, Reel 'Em In and Wheel of Fortune. Do be aware, however, that these polls are based on anecdotal evidence, and there are no statistical data to back them up.

Biggest game in town: Progressive slots, the game where machines are connected to one another and the jackpot rises as more people play. A huge overhead meter lets players keep track of the jackpot, which has reached more than $20 million in some cases. Two of the most popular wide-area progressive slots are Quartermania and Megabucks.

While prizes continue to rise, the odds of winning them remain long—very long. Ms. Crawford, for instance, was playing the nickel Megabucks slot, where the odds of winning the jackpot are about one in 40 million. *Make the slots more fun…*

Set a limit on how much to wager during any one session at the machines. Then cease playing when you've reached your limit or—if luck is with you—when you've won more than the amount you started with. Having self-discipline makes sense because no matter how long you play the slots, you are likely to lose many more games than you win. By quitting when you're ahead, you'll avoid the risk of a losing streak that takes away your winnings. Remember that the odds always favor the house, so if you play long enough, you're certain to lose more money than you win. If setting a limit is hard to do, remember Ms. Crawford. On the day she won, she had set a limit of $40 for the session and was down to her last $5. But if she had gone over her limit on the previous day, she might never have played on the day she struck it rich.

Frank Legato, a founding editor of *StrictlySlots* magazine, Galloway, New Jersey. Author of *How to Win Millions Playing Slot Machines!…Or Lose Trying* (Taylor Trade), Mr. Legato is also editor of *Global Gaming Business* magazine.

Untold Secrets to Winning at Texas Hold 'em

Texas Hold 'Em, the poker game that's favored by professional poker players, is rapidly becoming the favorite game of amateurs as well. The rules of Texas Hold 'Em are simple. Each player receives two cards facedown. After one round of betting, three cards are dealt face up for players to share (called the "flop"). Then there's a second round of betting, a fourth card up (the "turn"), a third round of betting, a final up card (the "river"), and one more round of betting. Players make their best five-card hands out of their two "pocket" cards and the five "community cards" face up on the table. While the rules are easy to learn, those who know Texas Hold 'Em only from watching TV tournaments often run into trouble when they try to play. *Here, winning strategies...*

• **Start tight.** When you watch poker on TV, the professionals seem to play lots of hands. That's because TV coverage shows only key hands. In most home games, the bets are small, so the best strategy is to play extremely "tight," folding most of the hands you're dealt. Play only when dealt one of the 10 best two-card starting hands—pairs of 7s or higher, or an ace-king or ace-queen. When you do get one of these great starting hands, always raise or reraise—don't just call (match a bet).

Exception: If a very conservative player already has made a big bet in front of you and you have a pair of 7s, 8s or 9s, you should fold. Playing only strong hands will boost your odds of survival while you learn and perfect your game, and you will earn a reputation for playing only great cards, which will make bluffing easier later on.

• **Raise after the flop even if it didn't help you.** The flop is the first three community cards turned over. Often, these won't be the cards you want—but your opponents may not want them either. Rather than not betting on a disappointing flop, make a bet to find out where you're at. Maybe your opponents will fold or call rather than raise, indicating that you might not be in such bad shape after all. (If a raise and a reraise are made before it's your turn to bet, fold if your hand isn't strong.)

Example: You hold 10-10, and the flop comes king-queen- 2. With two cards on the table higher than your 10s, someone might have hit a higher pair, putting you at a big disadvantage— or then again, maybe no one was holding a king or a queen. If you do not bet, someone else likely will—and you'll have to assume he/she made his hand and fold. If you do make a small bet and no one raises, it may tell you that you're still ahead and may confuse your opponents.

• **Learn to read your opponents.** Even after you fold, time at the poker table shouldn't be wasted. Pick one or two of your opponents and try to guess what cards they're holding based on their behavior and bets. Watch for patterns. Do they only raise on big hands? Do they act especially confident when they have nothing?

• **"Slow play" the occasional big hand.** Once your opponents get used to you betting big on the great hands, throw them a curve. If you have ace-ace or king-king, call before the flop. You might make the other players believe that your hand is weak and win a bigger pot. Even if you don't, you'll make it harder for them to figure out what you have later.

In no-limit or pot-limit Hold 'Em, in which pots can grow large, it might be worth seeing a flop (matching a bet before the flop) with a small pair if you can do so cheaply. The odds of hitting three of a kind still are against you, but if you do hit you might be able to build a big enough pot to make it worthwhile.

Phil Hellmuth, Jr., 13-time World Series of Poker champion and one of the most respected Texas Hold 'Em tournament players. He is author of *Phil Hellmuth's Texas Hold 'Em* (HarperCollins) and *Play Poker Like the Pros* (William Morrow). His Web site is *www.philhellmuth.com.*

BONUS REPORTS

Cash for Frequent-Flier Miles

Instead of using miles for flights or to buy items at airline "shopping malls," you can convert miles from some airlines into "virtual cash" that will be deposited into your PayPal account for purchases at online retailers. You also can move the cash into a PayPal-linked bank account. So far, American Airlines, US Airways and Aeroplan offer the service, using mileage manager Points.com to convert the miles. United Continental is expected to launch a program soon.

Caution: Converted miles may be worth less in virtual cash than when you use the miles to book flights.

Smart Money, *SmartMoney.com*

---

3 Ways to Save on Spring Break for Grown-Ups

Does any vacation period have a more salacious reputation than spring break? But you don't have to "go wild" to enjoy a great—and affordable—getaway...

1. Avoid the students. March is one of the most popular times for schools to schedule their spring breaks.

If you're not tied to a school's schedule, you will want to travel either in February (except over President's Day weekend, when prices are sky-high) or in April. If you are tied to a school schedule, avoid Cancun (Mexico), Panama City (Florida), Punta Cana (Dominican Republic), South Padre Island (Texas), Nassau (Bahamas) and Las Vegas.

2. Time your airfare purchase. A study by the Airlines Reporting Corporation (the organization that acts as middleman between travel agents and airlines) found that people who purchase airline tickets six weeks before their trips generally pay the least amount of money. Booking on a Tuesday or Wednesday also is a good strategy, as fare sales tend to be announced late in the day on Mondays and matched by the other carriers on Tuesdays.

3. Consider Europe or Central America. Airfares to Europe stay at their winter lows through March, as do hotel prices. Airfares to Central America are decent year-round, and the rate of exchange generally favors the dollar.

Pauline Frommer, a nationally syndicated newspaper columnist and radio talk show host. She is a member of the Frommer guidebook family and a two-time winner of the North American Travel Journalists Association's Guidebook of the Year award. *www.Frommers.com/pauline*

Luxury Cruises for Much Less

There is such an overwhelming array of itineraries, ships, packages and prices today that it can seem almost impossible to know whether you're getting the right cruise at the right price. *Here are more than a dozen smart strategies...*

• **Get an early bird discount.** If you book from six months to a year before departure, most cruise lines will discount their published retail rates. You'll also get your first choice of cabin category and location.

• **Look for off-season specials.** Cruise the Caribbean in the spring or summer, or try the Mediterranean in the winter. Avoid holidays and school vacation weeks. Of course, the trade-off may be the weather. For example, Athens can be chilly in the winter.

• **Take a "repositioning" cruise.** Some of the year's lowest rates can be found in the spring when ships relocate from their winter home ports in the Caribbean, Florida, Hawaii or Mexico to their summer bases in Europe, New York, Vancouver or Alaska.

• **Find a last-minute deal.** Because the cruise lines want to keep their ships full, you can sometimes get good discounts by booking only a month or two before departure, when a line finds it still has unsold cabins. The downside is that you can't be picky. Search newspaper ads and specific cruise sites or online cruise brokers.

• **Be flexible.** If you're willing to sail on a different date than you originally intended, you may be able to get the very same cabin on the same ship for significantly less money.

• **Look for the two-for-one promotions.** On some sailings, two passengers can share a cabin for the price of one.

• **Pick a port near home.** According to Terry Dale, former president of CLIA (Cruise Lines International Association), the trade organization for most of the major cruise lines, there are 32 home ports in North America today, and 75% of the US population lives within driving distance of one of them.

• **Snag a senior discount.** Cruise brokers frequently offer discounts to passengers over a certain age, usually 55, and their cabin mates of any age, especially on last-minute choices.

• **Go with a group.** Many lines will give you a reduced group rate. They may even toss in a free cabin if you organize a group.

• **Negotiate.** You might even get upgrades or extra amenities.

• **Take the kids—or grandkids—for nothing.** Off-season sailings will frequently offer to take children free. .

• **Share the cabin.** If you're traveling with friends or relatives, you can save a big bundle when they share your cabin by using the third and/or fourth berths.

• **Ask what's included.** Extra charges are not always included in the quoted price. Factor in all the port charges, taxes, handling fees and other costs before comparing deals.

• **Double check before you book.** Before booking a cruise, call the cruise line or broker or visit its Web site, because you may find a sale rate that's better than what you've decided upon. But make sure the cabin category and location and other important considerations are equivalent. Also try going to *www.cruisecompete. com*, an online "auction" service that asks dozens of independent agents to give you quotes on prices for the ship, travel dates and cabin category you've chosen so you can compare the fares and have a greater chance of getting the best deal.

Here are some of the specialized cruise discount sites...

• **icruise.com,** 800-427-8473.

• **www.cruise411.com,** 800-553-7090.

• **www.cruisesonly.com,** 800-278-4737.

• **cruise.com,** 888-333-3116.

You can also find discounts at *www.travelocity.com*, 888-872-8356, and *www.expedia.com*, 800-397-3342.

• **Consult a specialist.** After you've done your own research and have an idea of what you want, acquire the services of a travel agent or online retailer who specializes in cruises. An expert can help you sort everything out, find the best prices for your preferred itinerary, advise you on getting the best cabin and may even be able to throw in a few extras such as shipboard credit, shore excursions or a bottle of wine every night.

For a list of certified agents in your neighborhood, go to the Web site of CLIA at *www.cruising.org*.

Joan Rattner Heilman, an award-winning travel writer based in New York. She is author of *Unbelievably Good Deals and Great Adventures That You Absolutely Can't Get Unless You're Over 50* (McGraw-Hill).

4

Super Savings for Home and Family

Our Favorite Money Secrets

Buying Stocks Commission-Free...

The number of dividend reinvestment plans (DRIPs) that allow investors to make initial stock purchases directly has tripled since 1997. There now are more than 1,100 plans from US and foreign companies...and more of them than ever are open to those who are not yet shareholders.

Helpful: *www.dripinvestor.com* and *www.directinvesting.com*.

Charles B. Carlson, CFA , editor, *DRIP Investor*, 7412 Calumet Ave., Hammond, Indiana 46324.

Cash In on Insurance

Get cash for life insurance with a life settlement. Even policies with no cash value, such as term policies, may have value in life settlements. Viatical settlements are used when the insured individual is either terminally or chronically sick, for example, someone who took out insurance at age 60 and now is 72, has had a stroke and has heart disease, and can no longer afford policy premiums. Sale proceeds are not taxable. Senior settlements are used for anyone over age 65 who no longer needs his/her policy. Tax may be due on a portion of the proceeds. Life-settlement investors are interested in policies with face values of $250,000 or more. They might pay 10% to 30% of face value. Consult your financial adviser or attorney.

Keith Wegen, former vice president of finance, American Wealth Transfer Group LLP, Boulder, Colorado.

Pay for College While Shopping

U promise is a buyer-reward program that credits a portion of purchases from participating in-store and online retailers (hundreds and expanding) to your college-savings account, such as a 529 plan. Every time you shop within the Upromise network of retailers or use the Upromise credit card, you earn cash rebates between 1% and 10% of your total purchase that are automatically deposited into your educational investment account. Upromise offers similar benefits.

Information: Upromise, 888-434-9111, *www.upromise.com*.

Wait Until June to Buy Electronics

Retailers clear out their inventory to make room for newly upgraded equipment in January and June. Prices of older models typically fall by 10% or more.

Caution: Before buying, find out what new features are about to come to market. If they are ones you care about, buying an older model may not be a bargain after all.

Money, Time-Life Bldg., Rockefeller Center, New York City 10020.

Warranty Wisdom

E xtended warranties seldom make sense, even for big-ticket items. Warranties for appliances are least worthwhile because most appliances are now very reliable. Extended warranties only make sense for plasma TVs, laptop PCs and treadmills and elliptical trainers with warranties of less than one year.

Consumer Reports, 101 Truman Ave., Yonkers, New York 10703.

The Little-Known Way to Cut Your Utility Cost

Despite falling prices and various tax credits, the cost of solar energy systems that power your whole home can be fairly high. But for many home owners, solar still can be an environmentally friendly way to save lots of money, especially if you take advantage of attractive leasing arrangements or use solar just to power a water heater or an attic fan.

Here's what you need to know about home solar systems and whether one could save you money...

The Leasing Alternative

Some suppliers now are offering the option of leasing photovoltaic systems (also known as solar electric systems). Under these lease agreements, the supplier owns the equipment and collects all solar power tax incentives. The home owner makes a fixed monthly lease payment but, compared with buying the equipment, enjoys a greatly reduced up-front payment. In some cases, there is no up-front payment at all.

Leasing solar to provide your home's electricity could be a smart move for you if...

• **You pay less each month to lease the system** than you would pay for the electricity that the system replaces.

• **You don't want to spend $25,000 to $35,000** or much more up front to buy and install equipment.

Lease terms can vary greatly, so shop extensively before signing a contract. Make sure that the provider pays maintenance and repair expenses and that you can arrange to remove or relocate the system or transfer the lease if you sell the home.

Among the large solar companies offering leases are SolarCity (888-765-2489, *www.SolarCity.com*)...SunPower (800-786-7693, *http://us.SunPowerCorp.com*)...Sunrun (844-948-5400, *www.Sunrun.com*)...and Sungevity (866-786-4255, *www.Sungevity.com*).

Solar Water Heaters

Unlike whole-house photovoltaic systems, solar water heaters are economically viable. They qualify for the 30% federal tax credit. State incentives might be available as well—visit the US Department of Energy's Database of State Incentives for Renewables and Efficiency (*www.DSIREusa.org*) for details. Payback can come in as little as three to five years for households in Sunbelt states that have high electricity rates...or five to 10 years elsewhere.

Solar water heaters typically use rooftop solar collectors to heat an antifreeze solution, which is pumped to a heat exchanger where it warms water. Depending on your solar package, this warmed water can feed into a conventional water heater, which also can provide backup. Because the water entering the water heater is already quite warm, the heater doesn't consume as much electricity, gas or oil to heat the water to the desired temperature. The typical household can reduce water-heating costs by 50% to 80% without any loss of comfort.

Solar Attic Fans

Standard attic fans reduce your air-conditioning bills by blowing hot air out of the attic in warm weather, reducing the temperature differential between the attic and the living space below.

Problem: An electric attic fan can generate annual electricity bills of between $150 and $250.*

In contrast, solar-powered attic fans are money savers. They often cost just $500 to $750, plus $150 to $300 for installation. Installation is simple, so many home owners do it themselves—solar attic fans don't even have to be wired into the home's electrical system.

The fans qualify for the 30% federal tax credit and occasionally for state incentives, too. They tend to pay for themselves in two or three years in the Sunbelt and in three to six years elsewhere.

Leading makers include SunRise Solar Inc. (219-558-2211, *www.SunRiseSolar.net*) and Natural Light Energy Systems (800-363-9865, *www.SolarAtticFan.com*).

Jason Szumlanski, vice president and general manager for Fafco Solar Energy, based in Cape Coral, Florida, which has been installing solar-powered products since 1974 and deals with every major solar manufacturer. Szumlanski has worked in the solar industry since 1999, previously installing solar systems in the Caribbean.

*Prices subject to change.

Refinancing Secrets That Save You a Fortune

With mortgage rates near record lows, it's a great time to refinance—except for the fact that many home owners are having a tough time qualifying.

Lending standards have tightened greatly, making refinancing a challenge for home owners who have less-than-stellar credit ratings or high debt-to-income ratios. And reduced home values have left many home owners with insufficient home equity to qualify for refinancing.

But don't give up on today's good home mortgage deals—because there are solutions. *To clear major refinancing hurdles...*

Low Appraisal Value

In order to qualify for refinancing, your home's value typically must be appraised, and often nowadays the appraised value is so low that you end up with dramatically less equity in your home than you thought you had. The home's value even may be lower than the balance on your existing mortgage, leaving you "underwater." Lenders typically won't issue a refinance loan unless you have at least a 10% equity stake—meaning that you don't owe more than 90% of the home's value. A 20% equity stake typically is required to avoid paying private mortgage insurance (PMI).

What to do: There are four potential solutions if an appraisal suggests that refinancing (or refinancing without PMI) is impossible...

• **Get a second appraisal.** Ask the lender for a copy of the appraiser's report. It might be worth challenging the appraisal by paying for a second appraisal with the same lender if the lender is willing. Or you could shift to a different lender and get a new appraisal.

Using a second appraiser might be especially worthwhile if the first appraiser fell just short of the required value and if he/she failed to account for substantial improvements that you made to your home...or if he based the appraisal value largely on the sales prices of foreclosed or distressed homes or on homes in neighborhoods significantly less appealing than yours. This is not a step to take lightly, however—you'll typically have to pay $250 to $500 for a second appraisal.*

Helpful: If you believe that the original appraisal was flawed because it failed to properly account for the desirability of your neighborhood, ask your lender to select an appraiser based closer to where you live. This appraiser might better understand what the homes in your area are worth.

● **Do a "cash-in refinance."** Home owners who have sufficient cash can pay down their mortgages to reach the required equity levels.

Warning: If you have a second mortgage, you might have no choice but to pay this off to refinance.

● **Refinance through the Home Affordable Refinance Program (HARP).** If your mortgage is owned or guaranteed by Fannie Mae or Freddie Mac, the most recent version of the government's HARP program might allow you to refinance even if you are underwater or you have a limited equity position. The Web site *MakingHome Affordable.gov* can help you determine if your mortgage qualifies (select "Does Fannie or Freddie Own Your Loan?" from the "Tools" menu). If so, contact your mortgage servicer and ask if it is taking part in the HARP program. If your servicer is not taking part, you are allowed to refinance through a participating lender.

● **Refinance through the National Mortgage Settlement.** If your underwater mortgage is owned and serviced by Ally Financial, Bank of America, Citigroup, JPMorgan Chase or Wells Fargo, you might qualify for refinancing through a settlement that those mortgage issuers made in 2012 with government regulators to make up for questionable foreclosure practices. To be eligible, you must have a current interest rate of at least 5.25% and no late payments within the past 12 months...the property must be owner-occupied and underwater...and the new loan must slash at least $100 per month or be at least one-quarter of a percentage point lower than the borrower's existing rate, among other requirements. Contact your loan servicer for details.

*Prices subject to change.

Low Credit Score

It's possible to refinance with a FICO credit score as low as 620—but don't expect to be offered attractive refinancing terms these days unless your credit score is 740 or above.

What to do: Purchase a copy of your FICO credit score through MyFICO.com for $19.95, which includes a score and credit report based on information on file with one of the three main credit-reporting bureaus.

If your score is about 740 or lower, obtain copies of your credit reports from the three reporting bureaus—Equifax (*www.Equifax.com*), Experian (*www.Experian.com*) and Trans Union (*www.Trans Union.com*). Then contact those bureaus to correct any inaccurate information on the reports. Avoid running up big credit card balances, making payments late or applying for new credit in the months before applying to refinance a mortgage. Pay down credit card balances and other debts if possible.

If you cannot increase your credit score to 740, a Federal Housing Administration (FHA) mortgage might be the only way to refinance at an attractive rate. FHA-refinanced mortgages officially are available to those with credit scores as low as 580, but in practice, lenders make them difficult or expensive to obtain for home owners whose credit scores are below 620. Contact local mortgage lenders that deal with FHA loans for the details (select "Lender Locator" from the "Resources" menu at *www.HUD.gov*).

High Debt vs. Income

Several years ago, mortgage lenders considered a person's total debt-to-income ratio of 55% or even 60% sufficient to refinance—and many lenders often didn't even bother to confirm borrowers' income. These days, a ratio no higher than 28% is likely to be required—a small percentage of lenders will go as high as 43%—and every element of the borrower's financial situation will be scrutinized.

What to do: First, determine the ratio of your monthly debt payments to your monthly income, either using an online calculator (type "debt-to-income ratio calculator" into a search engine) or by asking a lender for help. If you've been paying down your mortgage for many years without borrowing against the value of the home, your debt-to-income ratio might not be as high as you fear. If you are slightly above the 38% mark, it might make sense to use liquid assets to pay down your debts enough to qualify for refinancing.

Lenders' recent emphasis on income verification can make refinancing particularly difficult for the self-employed. For these home owners, the best option often is refinancing through a credit union or community bank with which they have a long-standing relationship.

Keith Gumbinger, vice president of HSH Associates, publisher of mortgage and consumer loan information based in Riverdale, New Jersey. *www.HSH.com*

REPORT #25

Surprising Ways to Boost Your Credit Score

The higher your credit score (which ranges from 300 to 850), the lower the interest rate you'll be charged on many loans, including mortgages. Being prudent with your spending doesn't necessarily help your credit score. *To raise your score...*

• **Have several credit cards.** Otherwise, the lenders may have trouble deciding whether you are likely to pay multiple debts on time.

• **Watch your credit-use ratio.** A main factor in determining your score is the amount of your credit card balances versus credit limits. Keeping the balance below 30% of the limit on all of your cards will boost your score.

• **Don't consolidate debt onto a low-rate card and close the higher-rate account.** Doing so can raise your debt on the low-rate card above the 30% threshold. Instead, leave the high-rate card open. Pay off all your credit card balances, for example, with an installment loan, such as a bank personal loan, but leave the accounts open. The combination of decreasing your credit card balances and never being late on the installment will improve your credit score.

Evan Hendricks, editor of *Privacy Times,* and author of *Credit Scores & Credit Reports* (Privacy Times).

REPORT #26

Free Health Care Made Easy—
Free Hospital Care

If you don't have insurance coverage, even a very brief hospital stay can easily cost you tens of thousands of dollars and put you on the edge of bankruptcy. Fortunately, now there is something you can do. If you need hospital care but cannot afford it and have no insurance or if you have already been in the hospital and cannot afford to pay the bill, try calling the Hill-Burton Hotline. Through this program, hundreds of participating hospitals and other health facilities provide free or low-cost medical care. You could qualify for this assistance even if your income is up to double the poverty-level income guidelines and even if a medical bill has already been turned over to a collection agency.

For more information: Hill-Burton Hotline. 800-638-0742, *www.hrsa.gov/gethealthcare/affordable/hillburton.*

Free Medical Care

How would you like to have the finest medical care money can buy...and not spend one penny for it? That is exactly what thousands of people are doing every year thanks to the National Institutes of Health (NIH) Clinical Center. The NIH is funded by the federal government and is one of the nation's leading medical research centers. At any one time there may be more than 1,500 programs under way where researchers are studying the latest diseases, including all types of cancer, heart disease and diabetes, to mention a few. If your condition is one that is being studied, you might qualify for free medical care at the NIH hospital located in Bethesda, Maryland.

For more information: National Institutes of Health Clinical Center in Bethesda, Maryland. 800-411-1222, *www.cc.nih.gov.*

Free Eye Care

The community service pages of your local newspaper occasionally will run announcements by organizations such as the Kiwanis or Lions Clubs. They offer free eyeglasses and eye examinations to elderly people who couldn't afford them otherwise. Also, check with your state's Office of the Aging. There is a wide variety of eye-care programs offered, and many include free eye exams and free eyeglasses. To locate your state's office along with other resources, call 800-677-1116 or go to *www.eldercare.gov*.

Contact Lenses for Free

If you wear contact lenses or are thinking of getting them, Johnson & Johnson would like you to try their Acuvue contacts for free. Go to *www.acuvue.com*, fill out the information requested and a free-trial pair certificate will be sent out to you.

Free or Almost-Free Dental Care

There are more than 50 dental schools in the United States. All of them operate clinics that provide basic services at great savings. Services include checkups, cleaning, X-rays and fillings. More advanced services such as fitting bridges, dentures and implants may also be available. Student dentists do the work but are closely supervised by their professors.

Bonus: Care may even be free for conditions the professors are studying.

More information: To find a nearby dental school, try the Dental Education Program Search at *www.ada.org/267.aspx*.

REPORT #27

Never Pay Full Price for Medicine Again

Although the increasing costs of drug development continue to drive drug costs up, most people can save at least 50%.

Secret: Smart shopping, plus inside information on how to get the most medication for your money. *Whether you pay for drugs out-of-pocket or have drug coverage, here are ways to save...*

Price Shop

Prescription drug prices can vary by 25% or more from one pharmacy to the next. Don't assume that big chains have the best prices. Some smaller pharmacies scout out the cheapest drug wholesalers and pass the savings to consumers.

Smart idea: Price shop via phone. Call in the evening or during weekday afternoons when pharmacists are typically less busy.

Buy Online

You can save anywhere from 20% up to 50% buying drugs from online pharmacies, which have low overhead costs. The most reliable online pharmacies include Express Scripts, *www.express-scripts.com*, and Drugstore. com, *www.drugstore.com*.

Important: Buy only from online pharmacies that display the Verified Internet Pharmacy Provider Site (VIPPS) seal. The seal means that the company has been inspected and accredited by the National Association of the Boards of Pharmacy. Also, avoid online pharmacies that don't require a prescription. This is a sign that the company may be foreign or sells drugs illegally.

Request Older Drugs

Doctors don't admit it, but they're just as likely as patients to be influenced by slick drug marketing campaigns. Studies have shown that doctors are more likely to prescribe new drugs than older ones—even when there's clear evidence that the older drugs are just as effective and much less expensive than the newer ones.

Example: Millions of Americans with osteoarthritis switched to COX-2 inhibitors, such as *celecoxib* (Celebrex), when these drugs were introduced. For most patients, COX-2 inhibitors are no more effective than aspirin, acetaminophen or ibuprofen. Now studies show that these drugs may even increase risk for heart attack or stroke. What's more, a single dose of a COX-2 inhibitor might cost more than $2, compared with pennies for aspirin.

Smart idea: Ask your doctor to write prescriptions for older, less-expensive drugs unless there's a compelling medical reason to take a newer medication.

Generic Drugs

Brand-name prescription drugs can cost up to 85% more than generic drugs. If your doctor prescribes a specific brand-name drug, your pharmacist is permitted under state law to substitute a less expensive generic.

To find out if a generic is available: Go to the FDA's Web site, *www.fda.gov/cder/ob/default.htm*, for a list of all FDA-approved drugs and generic equivalents. Or use a drug reference book, such as the *Physicians' Desk Reference* (PDR Network), available in bookstores and libraries.

Medicare Drug Coverage

Everyone with Medicare coverage is now eligible to join a Medicare prescription drug plan and get insurance, which covers both brand-name and generic prescription drugs. For more information, visit the Medicare Web site at *www.medicare.gov* or call them at 800-633-4227.

Buy in Bulk

Check with your insurance plan to see if you can get a 90-day supply of your medications. You may be able to save the co-pay charges and dispensing fee charges.

Caution: Buy drugs in bulk only if you've already been taking them and know they work for you.

Split Pills

You can double the quantity of the doses in a single prescription by getting a higher-strength tablet and using a pill splitter to cut the pills into halves. A 100-milligram (mg) tablet often costs about the same as a 50-mg tablet of the same drug.

Important: Capsules cannot be split. Pills that have enteric coatings or other time-release mechanisms also should not be split. Ask your doctor or pharmacist if the pills that you take can be split. Do not use a kitchen knife to split your pills. Use a pill splitter, sold in pharmacies for about $5.

Marvin D. Shepherd, PhD, director of the Center for Pharmacoeconomic Studies and professor of health outcomes and pharmacy practice, University of Texas, Austin.

How I Saved $30,000 on My Wife's Hospital Bill

Recently, my wife had a medical procedure performed at her doctor's office. During the process, the doctor inadvertently nicked a blood vessel, which meant that my wife had to be taken to a nearby hospital so that the doctor could perform a 15-minute procedure to cauterize and close the injury. We entered the hospital at 10 pm and left three hours later when my wife had recovered from the anesthesia.

Two weeks later, we received a bill from the hospital for $34,000! I called the hospital and found out that the insurer had refused to pay because it had never approved an overnight admission. I let the insurer know that my wife was never admitted—she was at the hospital for only three hours. I refused to pay a penny of the bill. Our doctor backed us up by writing to the insurer and confirming that she had not been admitted. In the end, the bill was reduced to a still unbelievable $4,000, but the total amount was covered by our insurance.

These days, outrageous hospital bills are not uncommon. A recent media investigation found sky-high hospital charges such as $8 for one Tylenol caplet, $28 for a pair of latex gloves and $17 for an ice pack. And these hospital costs can be directly passed on to you if you get caught in one of the worst traps snaring an increasing number of people...

Admission vs. Observation

For many patients, the difference between being formally admitted to a hospital versus simply being held for observation can be thousands of dollars. There is really no difference between being "admitted" versus being "observed," except in the way a hospital can bill Medicare or some other insurer. If you are admitted, most charges are covered. If you are being observed, far less of the costs are covered.

Fearing that they might get audited by Medicare or private insurers for an improper admission, hospitals may try to protect themselves by keeping you for observation. And if you are held for observation, Medicare and other insurers will not pay for medicines (among other costs), such as diabetes or blood pressure drugs, that you may normally take outside the hospital while you are simply being observed. This is true even if you are being "observed" for up to 48 hours or even longer. As a result, hospitals may bill you whatever they want for those medications—often well above retail price.

And, because of the hospitals' fear of audits for improper admissions, the number of observation patients has more than tripled recently. Patients often are shocked by a huge bill that insurance doesn't cover.

My advice: If you are being kept at a hospital for more than a few hours (time in an emergency department does not count) or being kept overnight, insist that you be formally admitted. The doctor treating you can make the decision, and the hospital usually must comply. Because it's not always clear whether you or a family member is being observed or admitted, it's a good idea to ask the doctor, nurse or caseworker what the patient's status is.

Charles B. Inlander, a consumer advocate and health-care consultant based in Fogelsville, Pennsylvania. He was the founding president of the nonprofit People's Medical Society, a consumer advocacy organization that is credited with key improvements in the quality of US health care in the 1980s and 1990s, and is author or co-author of more than 20 consumer-health books. He is also a featured columnist in *BottomLine/Health, www.BottomLineHealth.com.*

REPORT #29

The Garden-Pest Problem-Solver

When spring comes, it is not long before critters invade your garden. Whether it's beetles feasting on your flowers or deer devouring your tomato plants, there are several ways to get rid of garden pests without resorting to the use of dangerous poisons to get rid of them. *Here 's how...*

Bugs

• **Aphids.** These tiny, green-gray bugs can suck the life from vegetables, flowers and tree leaves. They usually travel in large swarms so they can quickly devastate a garden. Aphids are repelled by the scent of citrus rind. Combine one tablespoon of freshly grated citrus rind with one pint of boiling water, steep overnight, strain the mixture through a coffee filter, then pour it into a spray bottle. Add three drops of dishwashing liquid, and spray affected plants and those nearby. Spray aphid-affected plants every five to seven days as long as the problem persists. Be sure to spray the undersides of leaves as well as the tops.

- **Japanese beetles.** These shiny, half-inch-long copper-colored beetles with green and white markings are particularly fond of rosebushes and grape and raspberry plants, but they will eat virtually any plant. To fight back, put soapy water in a wide bowl and hold it under the branches of beetle-affected plants. Gently shake the branches. Most of the beetles will drop into the bowl and drown. A long-term solution is to apply milky spore disease powder—available at garden stores—to your lawn near your garden as directed on the label. In two to five years, the disease will take hold, killing beetle grubs in the soil. The disease is harmless to humans, pets and beneficial insects.

- **Slugs and snails.** These pests eat holes through broad-leaf plants. To limit damage, place a few empty tuna or cat food cans in the soil up to their brims. Then pour beer into them. Slugs and snails are attracted to beer and drown in the cans. Dump the contents—beer and all—on your compost pile. Install beer traps in the spring before slugs and snails have a chance to reproduce.

Helpful: You will substantially reduce your garden's slug and snail population if you water in the morning. That way, the soil will be dry by night, when these creatures are active, robbing them of the moisture that they need to survive.

Animals

- **Deer.** Deer are naturally mistrustful of certain scents. You can hang cheesecloth bags of human hair (hair is available at salons and barber shops) around your garden. Dirty socks or bags of soap may also do the trick. Organic deer-repellent sprays, such as Deer Out and Deer Off, have odors that are offensive to deer but not to humans. You can expect to spend $25 and up per gallon at the garden store. Odor-based solutions such as these will not stop all deer, but they can cut plant loss in your garden by 30% to 50%. You also can create a living fence of these plants around your yard...

Flowers: Begonias, daffodils, foxglove, globe thistle, iris, lavender, marigolds, meadow saffron, peony, scented geraniums, snapdragons, stars of Persia, sweet alyssum, strawflowers, yarrow, zinnias.

Trees and bushes: American holly, boxwoods, Caucasian daphne, Sawara false cypress, Japanese pieris, northern red oak, pine, red osier dogwood, rugosa rose, spruce.

- **Rabbits.** Try scaring rabbits away with fake snakes. Cut an old garden hose into pieces, and place throughout your garden. If that doesn't work, another way to protect your garden is to construct a two- to three-foot-high chicken wire fence around it. The fence must extend at least six inches beneath the ground so rabbits can't burrow under it.

- **Voles.** These tiny rodents can consume close to their body weight in tubers and bulbs each day as they tunnel through your garden. When you plant bulbs, arrange a handful of sharp crushed gravel around them in the holes to keep voles away. Remove wood chips and mulch from the vicinity of young trees and shrubs in autumn so that voles have less cover during cold weather, when they eat mainly tree roots. Gardeners with serious vole problems can plant their crops in wooden frames with quarter-inch or smaller wire mesh stapled to the bottom. The mesh allows roots to grow out but prevents voles from tunneling in. Or grow daffodils, one of the few garden bulbs that voles (and squirrels) won't eat.

Christine Bucks, the editor of more than 20 gardening books, including *Great Garden Fix-Its: Organic Remedies for Everything from Aphids to Weeds* (Rodale), gardening solutions from dozens of successful gardeners.

REPORT #30

Save on Auto Insurance for Teens

To save on car insurance for your new teen driver, add him/her to your existing policy instead of taking out a new policy—

that way, your discounts pass through to him. Also, be sure to tell your insurer if your teen goes to college more than 100 miles away and does not take a car—your premiums will go down, but he still will be covered when home. Insist that your teen take a defensive-driving course, both for safety and to lower insurance rates. And, if you are buying your teen a car, get one with as many safety features as possible—and avoid sports cars and SUVs, which cost more to insure. Finally, shop around for insurance—costs for teens vary widely. When a teen turns 18, he may get a better deal by buying his own insurance policy.

CBSNews, *CBSNews.com.*

REPORT #31

Slash the Cost of Homeowner's Insurance by 40%!

If you update your alarm system or add a fire sprinkler system, it could lower home insurance costs by 15%, or $132 off the typical bill. Redoing electrical, plumbing, and heating and cooling systems in a way that would help protect against costly water claims and fire damage could lead to a discount of 40% or more. Be sure to let your insurer know whenever you make a significant change to your home's systems.

CNNMoney.com

REPORT #32

How to Protect Yourself from Hackers and Cyber Thieves

How secure is the wireless router that you use at home when sending online content through the air? Although it's commonly known that you need to protect a router with a password to prevent neighbors from borrowing your Internet connection, cyberthieves can easily circumvent these passwords if they are improperly configured.

If these cyberthieves—known as "sniffers" or "war drivers"—are within range of your Wi-Fi signal, typically 100 yards, they can send and/or download information over your connection once they breach your security. They also can use eavesdropping software to snoop through your e-mail...get the credit card numbers that you enter into Web sites...and get the user name and password you type in at your bank's Web site.

If your computer's hard drive isn't protected by special software, sniffers even can use your Internet connection to access your data files.

To protect yourself...

• **Consult the owner's manual** for your wireless router or call your Internet provider and ask for a technician to walk you through setting up a few security options. These options normally are left unactivated by the router's manufacturer, and most people don't bother to turn them on.

• **Turn on WPA2 encryption or better.** The old standard WEP encryption is easy to breach.

• **Set up MAC addressing.** This is a bit complicated, so if you can't figure it out through your owner's manuals, you may have to call a technician. This tool allows only computers that you specifically designate to access your wireless connection.

• **Protect your hard drive by enabling the firewall.** Both Windows-based and Apple Macintosh–based computers come with this software. It acts like an entryway lock that prevents other Internet users from accessing your hard drive.

John Sileo, president and CEO of The Sileo Group, a Denver-based identity theft prevention consulting and education provider that has worked with the Department of Defense, the Federal Reserve Bank and many other clients. He speaks internationally about online privacy, social-media exposure and digital reputation. He is author of *Privacy Means Profit: Prevent Identity Theft and Secure Your Bottom Line* (Wiley). *www.Sileo.com*

Check Your Phone Bill... You May Have Been "Crammed"

You could end up being charged for a service on your monthly mobile phone bill even though you never asked for it. This practice, called "cramming," occurs when a provider other than your phone company supplies you with ringtones, sports scores, weather updates, horoscopes and/or other unwanted services, and your phone company adds a charge to your bill, typically several dollars. (With landlines, cramming will usually show up as a line item for "miscellaneous" or "enhanced" services.)

The phone company keeps a portion of the revenue. Although three major telephone companies—AT&T, CenturyLink and Verizon—have agreed to cease most third-party billing for landlines, they continue for wireless unless you opt out.

Self-defense: Call your phone company now, and request that all third-party providers be blocked. Review your phone bills every month for surprise charges, often listed as "service charge," "other fees," "calling plan" or "membership."

Also, avoid calling "900" numbers, accepting anonymous collect calls and signing up for contests online via your cell phone, all common methods that vendors use to cram you.

If you do get crammed, call your service provider and demand a refund.

John Breyault, vice president of public policy, telecommunications and fraud at the National Consumers League, Washington, DC. *www.NCLnet.org*

Smarter Home Buying

Making an offer on a house? Include the following contingencies, so you can be sure the home lives up to your expectations. Insist on a home inspection by a professional inspector to uncover defects. Get extra inspections, if warranted by the general inspector, by structural engineers or other professionals. Make sure the house is insurable—insurers are reluctant to write policies on homes in certain areas, such as those prone to wildfires and mud slides.

Elizabeth Razzi, author of *The Fearless Home Buyer* (Stewart, Tabori & Chang).

Calling Customer Service?
Tips to Get Heard

Three new tricks worth trying when you must phone a customer service call center...

• **Get angry at the voice-recognition system** (but not at the human phone rep, which will only make him/her less likely to help you). Some companies are adding voice-recognition analysis technology that monitors callers' speech and transfers them to a person faster if they exhibit signs of anger or frustration—the companies hope to prevent that anger from growing worse.

• **Get specific with the voice-recognition system.** If your customer service call is answered by a computer, say the name of the product or service you need help with—even if this has not been listed among your options. With some systems, this will route you directly to the person you need to speak with, skipping the tedious phone tree. (If the system realizes that you have spoken but doesn't understand what you said, try saying something more general such as "agent" or "representative.")

• **Get a US-based rep if you have difficulty understanding accents.** An increasing percentage of large US companies are once again maintaining domestic call centers—but usually only as a small part of an international customer service network. If you don't get a US agent when you call and you have difficulty communicating, request to be transferred to one. Some companies allow this.

Adam Goldkamp, chief operating officer of Boston-based *GetHuman.com*, a free Web site that supplies consumers with toll-free customer service phone numbers and phone-tree tips for nearly 10,000 companies.

Package-Delivery Scam

Victims receive an e-mail that appears to be from the US Postal Service stating that a package could not be delivered. The e-mail says to click on a link in the message to arrange delivery or pickup—but clicking on this link loads a malicious virus that can steal information from the victim's computer. Forward spam e-mails to Spam@USPIS.gov.

Note: If there is a package for you, the postal service will leave a notice in your mailbox rather than send an e-mail.

Margaret D. Williams, national public information representative with the US Postal Inspection Service. *http://PostalInspectors.USPIS.gov*

Crooks Are Everywhere!

Some thieves wait in the theater parking lots, then break into cars when moviegoers enter the theater, steal car registrations to get addresses and burglarize homes during the films.

What to do: Always carry your car registration with you.

Crooks steal library cards, then borrow DVDs from libraries and sell them—leaving the cardholders liable for late fees or replacement costs.

What to do: Treat a library card as you would a credit card—if you find that it is missing, contact the library and put a hold on your library account.

AARP.org

What Your Car Dealer Doesn't Want You To Know

Buying a used luxury car can be a smart way to get the ride you have always wanted without breaking the bank—as long as you know what to look for.

Example: A new Mercedes-Benz S-Class sedan could sell for more than $91,000. A four-year-old version of essentially the same vehicle can be purchased for less than half the price of the new version. Today's luxury cars are extremely durable, so 50,000 miles on the odometer is no big deal. With gentle treatment and regular maintenance, a late-model luxury car can run well beyond 100,000 miles, largely free from trouble. Also, many of the most desirable premium models have classic looks that change little.

Example: Jaguar XJ Series or Range Rover. A five- or even 10-year-old model still looks very much like a brand-new one.

What to watch out for...

Used luxury vehicles can be very expensive to maintain, particularly if they haven't been scrupulously serviced according to the manufacturer's recommendations.

Example: Brake work on a high-end Mercedes-Benz can easily exceed $1,000.

Important: Have any used vehicle thoroughly evaluated— all systems checked out—ideally by a technician at a new-car dealership for that particular make. Expect to spend between $100 and $200 for this evaluation. Be wary of any used luxury car that doesn't have a complete record of service work—everything from oil and filter changes to other scheduled maintenance and repairs. If there are gaps in the record or it doesn't appear that a recommended or scheduled service was performed, ask for a price reduction equivalent to the cost of the service or pass on the deal.

Where to look...

Start by checking Edmunds.com, Autobytel.com and the National Automobile Dealers Association's used-car value guides (*www.nada.com*) to get a sense of the retail/wholesale prices for any car that you're interested in. Most major automakers have certified preowned (CPO) vehicle programs. Specific benefits include...

- **Manufacturer-backed extended warranty coverage,** which is generally much more inclusive than dealer-backed coverage.

- **Service records**—usually available from the time that the vehicle was new.

- **Vehicle inspection and service prior to resale.** This cuts down on some expenses that often are involved in buying a used car, such as new brakes or tires. Perhaps the best place to look for a properly maintained luxury car in good condition is in the classified ads of publications that cater to car club members devoted to the make/model you are interested in.

Recent Example: The BMW Car Club of America (800-878-9292, *www.bmwcca.org*) had several 2007 and 2008 models available for between $27,900 and $35,800. To find other high-end car clubs, simply Google the name of the car and the word "club."

Other resources: Publications that focus on specific makes can be found in major bookstores. *Hemmings Motor News* is a great general resource, available online (*www.hemmings.com*) and in print at major bookstores.

Classiest Used Cars

Some of my favorite used luxury cars...

• **1993 Cadillac Allante.** This beautiful convertible initially was plagued by an underpowered and problem-prone 4.1- and 4.5-liter V-8, but the engine was replaced in the final year of production. The '93s are the most desirable of the entire 1986–1993 production run. You can get a very nice Allante for less than $15,000.

• **Land Rover's legendary Range Rover 4.6 HSE.** The loaded 2005 model can go for around $10,000. A new Range Rover costs over $79,000.

• **Lexus LS 430 and LS 460.** These exceptionally well-built, durable luxury sedans are some of the best used buys. A 2004 LS 430 can be found for about $13,000—a new LS sedan costs about $70,000.

• **1987-1991 Lincoln Mark VII LSC.** This is America's answer to the Mercedes-Benz SL. These large, sophisticated-looking coupes all feature powerful five-liter V-8s...high-capacity disc brakes... and air-ride suspension. Well-maintained examples can be found for just a few thousand dollars.

• **Mercedes E-Class Turbo Diesel was one of the best midsize luxury sedans around.** A 1999 E300 Turbo Diesel can be found for around $8,000. The base price of a new E-Class with a gas V-8 is about $52,000.

Eric Peters, automotive columnist in Washington, DC. He is author of *Automotive Atrocities!* (MBI). His Web site is *http://ericpetersautos.com.*

5

Health and Happiness Secrets

REPORT #33

Simple Ways to Cut Your Disease Risk by 80%

If you were to boil down all of our medical wisdom to just a few words, you would already know them—exercise, eat well, don't smoke and maintain a healthy weight. But a shocking number of people are not following through. Only 9% of adults meet all of the criteria for a healthy lifestyle—that's right, only 9%!

The study, which looked at more than 23,000 participants between the ages of 35 and 65, found that those who improved any one of the factors above were 50% less likely to develop a chronic disease. Those who did all four at the start of the study had a nearly 80% reduced risk for any chronic disease.

So why aren't we doing what we should? Because it seems too hard! *Here are little ways to get started…*

• **Eat popcorn.** Even if your diet is mainly healthy, you still will gain weight if you don't keep an eye on portion sizes. This is particularly important for those who eat processed foods, which typically pack a lot of calories into surprisingly small servings.

My advice: Eat foods with a high satiety index. Even small servings of these foods will fill you up, so you consume fewer calories. Popcorn is a good example. It contains a lot of air, which takes up space in the stomach. (But avoid chemical-laden packaged micro-wave popcorn.)

Other high-satiety foods include those with a lot of water (such as soup or fruits)...protein (beans, lean meats, nuts, etc.)... and low-glycemic foods (such as sweet potatoes or whole grains), which are absorbed slowly into the bloodstream.

• **Get the right fiber.** The Centers for Disease Control and Prevention has reported that the prevalence of diabetes has increased by 45% in the last 20 years, with the greatest increase occurring in people 65 years old and older.

Self-defense: Studies have shown that soluble fiber—the type found in beans, lentils, berries, vegetables and whole grains, particularly oats—slows the rate at which sugar enters the bloodstream. If you eat oatmeal for breakfast, you will have a lower blood sugar response to whatever you eat for lunch.

My advice: In addition to adding more fiber to your diet—the optimal amount is 35 grams or more a day—include foods with a high percentage of soluble fiber. For example, add a whole grain, an apple or avocado, raw spinach or cooked broccoli, or a bean dish to every meal.

• **Think movement, not exercise.** Even people who exercise often approach it as a formal, and not particularly fun, activity. This mind-set might explain why lack of physical activity now accounts for nearly 10% of premature deaths in the world each year. The accumulation of 20 to 30 minutes of daily physical activity provides up to 85% of the cardiovascular benefits of hard exercise.

My advice: Think about what you already do—and do those things more often. Dancing is good exercise. So is a stroll through a park. An hour spent gardening counts. So does moving furniture...a bike ride...and a yoga class.

David L. Katz, MD, MPH, internist and preventive medicine specialist. He is co-founder and director of the Yale Prevention Research Center and clinical instructor at the Yale School of Medicine, both in New Haven. He is author, with Stacey Colino, of the upcoming book *Disease-Proof: The Remarkable Truth About What Makes Us Well* (Hudson Street).

How to Cancer-Proof Your Body

People often think that cancer is out of their hands because it is "genetic." In fact, lifestyle decisions are much more important in determining who gets cancer—and who does not. Even if your genes do place you at risk for cancer, 60% to 70% of all malignancies can be avoided by paying attention to four powerful lifestyle factors—diet, weight control, exercise and not smoking.

If You Make Just One Change

Eating a plant-based diet is the single most important thing you can do to help lower your cancer risk. Foods should be minimally processed and eaten as close to their natural state as possible. Processed foods may have lost some of their nutritional value.

Example: Eat a potato rather than chips or french fries. Also limit intake of foods with added sugar, such as soft drinks and sweetened cereals. If you eat red meat regularly, try to have no more than three ounces per day. Eating at least five servings—about one-half cup each—of fruits or vegetables every day can decrease your risk of developing cancer by 20%.

Other Important Steps

● **Maintain a healthful weight, and be physically active.** Try not to gain too much weight after reaching your full height (at about age 18 for women...24 for men). Start by walking every day—working your way up to a brisk, one-hour walk daily. In addition, work up a sweat by engaging in some form of vigorous physical activity for at least one hour each week.

● **Select foods that are low in fat and salt.** Limit your intake of fatty foods. Use a moderate amount of monounsaturated oils, such as olive and canola. Avoid animal fat and hydrogenated fat, which is commonly found in shortening, margarine and bakery items. Watch those snack foods, salty condiments and pickles.

● **Prepare and store foods safely.** Keep cold foods cold and hot foods hot. If you eat meat, avoid charring it. Limit your intake of cured or smoked meat. Take precautions when grilling.

- **Avoid tobacco in any form.**

Cancer Risk Factors

Anticancer precautions are particularly important for all individuals at increased risk for cancer. *These risk factors include...* *

- **Family history of genetically linked types of cancer,** such as breast, ovarian and colon cancers.
- **Inflammatory bowel disease.**
- **Human papillomavirus (HPV) infection.**
- **Alcoholism.**
- **Hepatitis B or C virus (HBV/HCV).**

Additional risk factors for women...

- **First menstrual period before the age of 12.**
- **First child born after age 30.**
- **Childless and over age 50.**
- **Postmenopausal and on hormone-replacement therapy.**

*This information is based on a major study by the American Institute for Cancer Research that reviewed more than 4,500 studies to determine the relationships among diet, lifestyle and cancer risk.

Melanie Polk, RD, former director, nutrition education, American Institute for Cancer Research, 1759 R St. NW, Washington, DC 20009. *www.aicr.org*

REPORT #35

What Vitamin Makers Don't Tell You

The best place to buy vitamins is in a natural-foods store or other place that focuses on dietary supplements. Their products, unlike those at chain pharmacies, are most likely to contain the most potent forms—and no artificial colors or preservatives. *What to look for...*

- **Vitamin E.** The gamma tocopherol form is natural and more potent than dl-alpha tocopherol, the synthetic form.

- **Vitamin C.** The best forms come from rose hips, tapioca or other natural sources. In addition to ascorbic acid, they contain powerful bioflavonoids.

- **Vitamin B.** Supplements should contain equal amounts of B-1 (thiamine), B-2 (riboflavin) and B-6 (pyridoxine). The best ones are made from rice, yeast or other natural products.

Also important...

- **If possible, buy vitamins in dark-colored or opaque containers.** They will last longer.

- **Don't purchase more than a two-month supply at a time.** And make sure that products are not past their expiration dates.

- **Always keep vitamins away from moisture.** When you open the container, remove any cotton balls, which absorb moisture and can cause vitamins to disintegrate. Don't store vitamins in the bathroom or refrigerator unless the label tells you to

Earl Mindell, RPh, PhD, nutritionist in Beverly Hills, California, and author of *New Vitamin Bible* (Hachette) and *Prescription Alternatives* (McGraw-Hill).

REPORT #36

Say Goodbye to Hot Flashes and Night Sweats!

Try eating more soy. In a study, menopausal women who added 20 grams of soy powder per day (about four tablespoons) to their diets reported reduced severity of hot flashes and night sweats.

Bonus: Their cholesterol levels also fell.

Theory: Soy contains isoflavones, which are compounds that mimic the beneficial effects of estrogen with less risks. Estrogen-replacement therapy raises the risk of breast and ovarian cancer, heart disease and stroke. Soy powder, available at health food stores, can be added to juice, cereals and other foods.

Gregory L. Burke, MD, professor and director, division of public health sciences, Wake Forest University School of Medicine in Winston-Salem, North Carolina.

Hidden Toxins in Your Home

If you don't think that toxins are lurking, undetected and invisible in your home, this fact will make you sit up and take notice. The air inside our homes may be anywhere from two to 100 times more polluted than the air just beyond our front doors, according to the Environmental Protection Agency. How could this be? It turns out that the air we breathe in our homes may contain contaminants, fungi or chemical by-products that can harm our health.

It is easy to feel overwhelmed when reading about all of these dangers, but the good news is that by taking simple steps you can stay ahead of the game in terms of protecting yourself and your family...

The Threat: Mold

This may come as no surprise to you: It is estimated that about half of all US homes are contaminated with mold. Mold (and its cousin, mildew) are fungi, and their spores are everywhere, both indoors and out. But mold needs moisture to grow, which is why it thrives wherever there is moisture in your home—in large areas, such as damp basements, or even in small piles of damp clothing.

If you are exposed long enough—mainly through inhaling mold spores—you may become allergic, experiencing a chronic runny nose, red eyes, itchy skin rashes, sneezing and asthma. Some types of mold produce secondary compounds called mycotoxins that can even cause pneumonia or trigger autoimmune illness such as arthritis.

What you may not know: Moisture control must begin promptly—you have about 24 to 48 hours to completely dry out wet areas or dampness before mold starts to grow. This time frame can help you cope with small areas of moisture and reduce your exposure to mold.

Examples: It's important to quickly dry wet clothes left in a gym bag or in a washer or dryer...damp windowsills...and spills in the refrigerator. When cleaning pillows and duvets, make sure to wash and dry them according to manufacturers' instructions—otherwise the filler may retain moisture, encouraging mold growth.

To remove small areas of mold (it can be black, brown, green, yellow or white and may have an acrid smell), scrub them with a mixture of one-eighth cup of laundry detergent, a cup of bleach and a gallon of water.

Mold on a wall often is a sign that mold is also within the wall, so you'll need to consult a professional about removal, especially if the area is larger than 10 square feet.

The Threat: Water

Up to 700 chemicals have been found in tap water, many of which have been linked with cancer, hypothyroidism and immune system damage. You can find out details about the water in your area by going to *www.EWG.org/tap-water* and entering your Zip code. At this site, you will find out about some of the contaminants in your tap water, such as lead and barium. You also will find out which ones might exceed health guidelines. In high amounts, these contaminants may cause brain damage, cancer and liver and kidney damage.

What you may not know: Contaminants in tap water, when heated, can become inhalable gasses in the shower. When inhaled while showering, chloramines and chlorine, which often are used to treat drinking water, vaporize and can raise risk for bladder cancer, hypertension, allergies and lung damage.

To prevent exposure to inhalable gasses and chlorine, buy a showerhead filter. It should remove chloramines, chlorine, lead, mercury and barium.

Good brand: Santé (*www.SanteforHealth.com*, various models are available for under $200*).

The Threat: Radon

Radon is an invisible, odorless toxin created naturally during the breakdown of uranium in soil, rock and water. This radioactive gas can sneak into your home via cracks in the foundation. It is the number-one cause of lung cancer among nonsmokers—and smokers are even more susceptible.

Most people know about testing for radon when they sell or buy a home. The EPA recommends in-home testing for anyone

*Prices subject to change.

who lives in a basement or on the ground, first or second floors. You can purchase an affordable short-term test kit. (One brand to try is Kidde Radon Detection Kit, under $20).

Long-term radon testing kits take into account weather variations and humidity levels that can throw off short-term results. If a short-term kit reveals elevated levels, then you need to do long-term testing.

What you may not know: The EPA sets an acceptable level of radon at anything below 4 picocuries per liter (pCi/L). However, in 2009 the World Health Organization determined that a dangerous level of radon was 2.7 pCi/L or higher.

My advice: Do periodic testing and keep 2.7 in mind for acceptable radon levels.

Mitchell Gaynor, MD, assistant clinical professor of medicine at Weill Medical College of Cornell University in New York City. He is the founder and president of Gaynor Integrative Oncology and is board-certified in oncology, hematology and internal medicine. He has written several books, including one about environmental dangers.

REPORT #38

Sleep Apnea Could Be Killing You While You Sleep…Millions Have It and Most Don't Even Know It

Twenty-eight million Americans have sleep apnea, a sleep disorder in which breathing repeatedly stops and starts. More than 80% of these people don't know they have it. And every year, an estimated 38,000 Americans die in their sleep because sleep apnea has exacerbated a circulatory problem, causing a fatal heart attack or stroke.

Bottom line: Diagnosing and treating sleep apnea can save your life. And now there's an exciting new treatment that's available. *What you need to know…*

Do You Have It?

Risk factors for obstructive sleep apnea include snoring (a sign of a thickened soft palate), being male, being 65 or older (for women, risk rises after menopause) and obesity. But some people with sleep apnea have none of those risk factors.

Several daytime symptoms are possible signs of sleep apnea. You might wake up with a headache and a dry mouth. You could be intensely tired during the day—even falling asleep at a red light. You might be irritable and depressed and find it hard to think clearly.

If your doctor suspects sleep apnea, he may recommend a "sleep study" conducted in a sleep disorder center. This overnight test—polysomnography—monitors and measures breathing patterns, blood oxygen levels, arm and leg movement, and heart, lung and brain activity. *But there are several downsides to a study in a sleep center…*

- **It's expensive, costing $1,500 to $2,500*** —which could be out-of-pocket if your insurance has a high deductible.

- **It's inconvenient.** You are spending the night in a strange place with a video camera focused on you and personnel walking in and out.

Instead, I often recommend a sleep study at home. Using a portable device, it provides the same information as a study at a center—for a fraction of the cost ($250 to $600). It is becoming the preferred method of testing for many doctors and often is covered by insurance. I prefer the home test by SleepQuest.

For more information: 877-672-8378, *www.SleepQuest.com.*

Exciting New Treatment

Up until now, the standard treatment for sleep apnea has been a continuous positive airway pressure (CPAP) machine. This device uses tubing and a mask worn over the nose…over the nose and mouth…or directly in the nose (via what is called a nasal pillow). The mask continuously pumps air into the airway, preventing the soft palate from sagging. But the mask often is uncomfortable. In one study, nearly half of people prescribed a CPAP device stopped using it within one to three weeks.

The exciting news is that there's a convenient treatment for sleep apnea called Provent. A small, disposable patch fits over each nostril. The treatment uses your own breathing to create expiratory positive airway pressure (EPAP)—just enough to keep the throat open.

*Prices subject to change.

Recent scientific evidence: In a three-month study involving 250 people with sleep apnea, 127 used Provent and 123 used a fake, look-alike device. The people using Provent had a 43% decrease in nighttime apnea events, compared with a 10% decrease for those in the fake group. Over three months, there was also a significant decrease in daytime sleepiness among Provent users.

A 30-day supply of the patches costs about $70. They are prescription-only and currently are not covered by insurance or Medicare.

My perspective: Provent is an excellent new option for many people with obstructive sleep apnea, but it is not for mouth breathers, people with nasal allergies or those with severe apnea.

Information: 888-757-9355, *http://Provent.ActiveHealthCare. com.*

Customized Mouth Guard

If the nasal patch is not an option for you, a customized oral appliance may be best. It moves the lower jaw forward, opening the throat. It usually is covered by insurance, either partially or totally.

Red flag: Over-the-counter oral appliances for snoring are available, but for optimal results, you need an oral appliance created for your mouth and jaw by a dentist trained to make such a device.

Important: No matter which device you use, you need to get tested first and then retested after you start using the device to make sure that you are getting the oxygen you need.

Lifestyle Changes

Self-care strategies...

• **Sleep on your side.** This helps keep airways open.

• **Lose weight, because extra pounds mean extra tissue in the throat.** Just a 10% weight loss can decrease apnea events by 26%. However, thin people and children can have apnea, too.

• **Don't drink alcohol within three hours of going to bed.** It relaxes the airway.

- **Sing some vowels.** In a study by UK researchers, three months of singing lessons helped decrease snoring, which could in turn decrease apnea.

What to do: Sing the long vowel sounds a-a-a-e-e-e, taking two or three seconds to sing each vowel. Do this once or twice every day for five minutes a session.

Chris Meletis, ND, former chief medical officer for the National College of Naturopathic Medicine and currently the executive director of the Institute for Healthy Aging and a physician on the staff of Beaverton Naturopathic Medicine in Oregon. He is author of numerous books on health and healing, including *The Hyaluronic Acid Miracle* (Freedom Press). *www.DrMeletis.com*

REPORT #39

Self-Defense Against Side Effects

Women have a 50% to 70% greater risk of developing an adverse drug reaction than men, according to the Society for Women's Health Research (SWHR).

Why are women are greater risk? Marianne Legato, MD, founder and director of The Partnership for Gender-Specific Medicine at Columbia University in New York City, explained that women and men often have disparate reactions to drugs due to differences in hormones, metabolism, biochemistry and anatomy—and even factors such as oral contraceptive use or where a woman is in her menstrual cycle can make a difference.

Unfortunately, some problems become evident only after a drug has been in use for a while. For instance, Dr. Legato pointed out that the antihistamine *terfenadine* (Seldane) was on the market for years before it was found to cause potentially fatal disruptions in cardiac rhythm, especially in women, and was banned by the FDA. This was not an isolated event. According to the SWHR, of the 10 prescription drugs withdrawn from the US market between 1997 and 2000, eight caused statistically greater health risks for women than men. What's more, even when information is available on a drug's dangers, you can't assume that every doctor is aware of all potential side effects, especially the gender-specific ones.

More than half of all adverse drug reactions treated in hospitals and emergency facilities are preventable, according to the

International Pharmaceutical Federation. Such prevention requires patients to be proactive in assessing the pros and cons before using a prescription or over-the-counter drug that is new to them. So when your doctor says, "Take this," be sure to ask…

• **Why do I need to take this drug?** Your doctor should describe what the medication is intended to do…clarify why this drug is better than any other…and explain why medication is more appropriate for you than any nondrug treatment available.

• **What are the possible side effects?** There is no such thing as a drug with zero potential adverse effects, Dr. Legato noted. Your physician should review not only the most common side effects, but also the warning signs of a dangerous reaction (no matter how rare) and outline what to do (call the doctor, go to the emergency room) if problems arise.

• **Did the clinical trials for this drug include women?** If the answer is yes, find out how well the drug worked for women specifically and whether females were more prone to problems. If the answer is no, ask what is known about how women react to this drug.

• **How long has this drug been on the market?** Unless absolutely necessary, try to avoid taking a brand new medication until its full effects are better known.

• **What is your doctor's own experience in prescribing this drug?** For instance, has your doctor received any complaints about side effects from his other patients? It is best if your doctor has firsthand knowledge of the medication, rather than prescribing it based solely on its reputation.

• **Could this drug interact with other medications?** Women consume more medications than men, and the use of multiple medications is higher in women, the SWHR reports. Obviously, the more drugs you take, the higher the risk for potentially dangerous interactions. With your doctor, review all prescription and nonprescription drugs—as well as supplements—that you take regularly or even occasionally. If there is a potential for interaction, discuss alternatives to the new medication or needed alterations to your current regimen.

Once you get home, it's prudent to do further research using a reliable Web site such as the National Library of Medicine Drug Information Portal *(http://druginfo.NLM.NIH.gov)*. Or try the new interactive online tool called the Question Builder *(www.AHRQ.*

gov) from the Agency for Healthcare Research and Quality, designed to help patients ask questions that will optimize their care, including safe and appropriate medication use. If you learn something about your new drug that concerns you, call your doctor to discuss it.

Marianne Legato, MD, a professor of clinical medicine and founder and director of The Partnership for Gender-Specific Medicine at Columbia University in New York City. She also is author of numerous books, including *Eve's Rib: The Groundbreaking Guide to Women's Health* (Three Rivers). She has received numerous awards, including a Research Career Development Award presented by the National Institutes of Health.

REPORT #40

The High Blood Pressure Breakthrough

For most Americans, a steaming hot bath or shower is a daily routine. But for more than 150 years, numerous Europeans have used invigorating cold showers and swims to promote good health. Scientific evidence and numerous case histories support the use of "cold-water therapy" as an adjunct to standard treatments for frequent colds, insomnia, high blood pressure—even cancer and other serious disorders.

How It Began

Cold-water treatment was first popularized in Germany by the priest Sebastian Kneipp (1821–1897). In the winter of 1849, Kneipp successfully combatted then-incurable tuberculosis by plunging several times weekly into the frigid Danube River. His 1886 book, *My Water Cure*, became an international best-seller.

The Mechanism

When practiced for at least four weeks, cold-water therapy...

• **Stabilizes blood pressure.** Cold water triggers the autonomic nervous system—which controls involuntary functions, such as heartbeat and breathing—to raise blood pressure, increase heart rate and constrict blood vessels. The autonomic responses strengthen with each exposure. This stabilizes blood pressure, improves circulation and balances other bodily functions, such as the sleep/wake cycle.

- **Enhances immunity.** Cold water triggers the release of cytokines and other hormone-like substances that are key to improving immune function.

A recent finding: Breast cancer patients who underwent four weeks of cold-water therapy experienced significant gains in their levels of disease-fighting white blood cells, according to a German study.

- **Reduces pain.** Cold causes the body to release endorphins, hormones with proven pain-fighting properties.

- **Improves moods.** Cold water activates sensory nerves that lead to the brain. A cold, exhilarating shower can be emotionally uplifting and prime a person for new experiences.

The Regimen

To gain the benefits of cold-water therapy at home, begin with your usual warm shower. When you're finished, step out of the water stream and turn off the hot water. Leave the cold water running.* Start by wetting your feet first. Next, expose your hands and face to the cold water.

Important: Jumping into the water all at once may hinder circulation. Finally, step under the shower. Let the cold water run over your scalp, face, the front of your body and then down your back. You can begin by taking a cold shower that lasts only a couple of seconds. After a month, the entire process should last no more than 40 seconds. Work up to whatever is comfortable for you.

If you can't tolerate the cold: Keep the water cold but expose only your feet, hands and face. Gradually increase the duration and area of exposure.

Caution: People who are very thin or frail may be unable to tolerate cold showers in the beginning. If you do not feel warm and invigorated after the shower, decrease the length of your next cold shower. If you still don't feel warm within minutes, forgo cold showers. Instead, condition your body with cold sponge baths of the feet, hands, face—and then the rest of your body—after your warm shower. Do not try cold-water therapy if you suffer from an acute illness, such

*If you have a muscle disorder or chronic pain, check with your doctor before starting this technique as it could worsen these conditions.

as intense back pain, or have hardening of the arteries (atherosclerosis)…Raynaud's disease…or high blood pressure not controlled by medication. Cold water causes a spike in blood pressure, which can be dangerous for those who have conditions such as unmanaged hypertension. The therapy can be safely used to decrease mildly elevated blood pressure or to raise low blood pressure.

If you have questions about your blood pressure: See your doctor for a blood pressure test before starting a coldwater regimen.

Alexa Fleckenstein, MD, board-certified internist who practices conventional and complementary medicine, Boston. Dr. Fleckenstein holds a German subspecialty degree in natural medicine.

REPORT #41

Stop Diabetes in Its Tracks

With all the devastating complications of diabetes, such as heart disease, stroke, dementia and blindness, you might assume that most doctors are doing everything possible to catch this disease in its earliest stages. Not so.

Problem: There are currently no national guidelines for screening and treating diabetes before it reaches a full-blown stage.

Research clearly shows that the damage caused by diabetes begins years—and sometimes decades—earlier, but standard medical practice has not yet caught up with the newest findings on this disease.

Fortunately, there are scientifically proven ways to identify and correct the root causes of diabetes so that you never develop the disease itself.

When the Problem Starts

Diabetes is diagnosed when blood sugar (or glucose) levels reach 126 milligrams per deciliter (mg/dL) and above. "Prediabetes" is defined as blood sugar levels that are higher than normal but not high enough to indicate diabetes. Normal blood sugar levels are less than 100 mg/dL.

What most people don't know: Although most doctors routinely test blood sugar to detect diabetes, it's quite common to have a normal level and still have diabesity, a condition typically marked by obesity and other changes in the body that can lead to the same complications (such as heart disease, stroke and cancer) as full-fledged diabetes.

Important: Even if you're not diabetic, having "belly fat"—for example, a waist circumference of more than 35 inches in women and more than 40 inches in men—often has many of the same dangerous effects on the body as diabetes.

Important finding: In a landmark study in Europe, researchers looked at 22,000 people and found that those with blood sugar levels of just 95 mg/dL—a level that's generally considered healthy—already had significant risks for heart disease and other complications.

An Earlier Clue

Even though we've all been told that high blood sugar is the telltale sign of diabetes, insulin levels are, in fact, a more important hallmark that a person is in the early stages of the "diabetes continuum."

High blood sugar is typically blamed on a lack of insulin—or insulin that doesn't work efficiently. However, too much insulin is actually the best marker of the stages leading up to prediabetes and diabetes.

Why is high insulin so important? In most cases, it means that you have insulin resistance, a condition in which your body's cells aren't responding to insulin's effects. As a result, your body churns out more insulin than it normally would.

Once you have insulin resistance, you've set the stage to develop abdominal obesity, artery-damaging inflammation and other conditions that increasingly raise your risk for prediabetes and diabetes.

A Better Approach

Because doctors focus on prediabetes and diabetes—conditions detected with a blood sugar test—they tend to miss the earlier signs of diabesity. *A better approach...*

• **Test insulin as well.** The standard diabetes test is to measure blood sugar after fasting for eight or more hours. The problem with this method is that blood sugar is the last thing to rise. Insulin rises first when you have diabesity.

My advice: Ask your doctor for a two-hour glucose tolerance test. With this test, your glucose levels are measured before and after consuming a sugary drink—but ask your doctor to also measure your insulin levels before and after consuming the drink.

What to look for: Your fasting blood sugar should be less than 80 mg/dL...two hours later, it shouldn't be higher than 120 mg/dL. Your fasting insulin should be 2 international units per deciliter (IU/dL) to 5 IU/dL—anything higher indicates that you might have diabesity. Two hours later, your insulin should be less than 30 IU/dL.

Cost: $50 to $100 (usually covered by insurance).* I advise all patients to have this test every three to five years...and annually for a person who is trying to reverse diabetes.

Steps to Beat Diabesity

With the appropriate lifestyle changes, most people can naturally reduce insulin as well as risk for diabesity-related complications, such as heart disease.

Example: The well-respected Diabetes Prevention Program sponsored by the National Institutes of Health found that overweight people who improved their diets and walked just 20 to 30 minutes a day lost modest amounts of weight and were 58% less likely to develop diabetes. *You can reduce your risk even more by following these steps...*

• **Manage your glycemic load.** The glycemic index measures how quickly different foods elevate blood sugar and insulin. A high-glycemic slice of white bread, for example, triggers a very rapid insulin response, which in turn promotes abdominal weight gain and the risk for diabesity.

My advice: Look at your overall diet and try to balance higher-glycemic foods with lower-glycemic foods. In general, foods that are minimally processed—fresh vegetables, legumes, fish, etc.—are lower on the glycemic index. These foods are ideal because they cause only gradual rises in blood sugar and insulin.

• **Eat nonwheat grains.** Many people try to improve their diets by eating whole-wheat rather than processed white bread or pasta. It doesn't help.

*Prices subject to change.

Fact: Two slices of whole-wheat bread will raise blood sugar more than two tablespoons of white sugar. If you already have diabetes, two slices of white or whole-wheat bread will raise your blood sugar by 70 mg/dL to 120 mg/dL. Wheat also triggers inflammation...stimulates the storage of abdominal fat...and increases the risk for liver damage.

These ill effects occur because the wheat that's produced today is different from the natural grain. With selective breeding and hybridization, today's wheat is high in amylopectin A, which is naturally fattening. It also contains an inflammatory form of gluten along with short forms of protein, known as exorphins, which are literally addictive.

Best: Instead of white or whole-wheat bread and pasta, switch to nonwheat grains such as brown or black rice, quinoa, buckwheat or amaranth. They're easy to cook, taste good—and they don't have any of the negative effects. Small red russet potatoes also are acceptable.

• **Give up liquid calories.** The average American gets 175 calories a day from sugar-sweetened beverages. Because these calories are in addition to calories from solid food, they can potentially cause weight gain of 18 pounds a year. The Harvard Nurses' Health Study found that women who drank one sugar-sweetened soft drink a day had an 82% increased risk of developing diabetes within four years.

Moderation rarely works with soft drinks because sugar is addictive. It activates the same brain receptors that are stimulated by heroin.

My advice: Switch completely to water. A cup of unsweetened coffee or tea daily is acceptable, but water should be your main source of fluids.

Bonus: People who are trying to lose weight can lose 44% more in 12 weeks just by drinking a glass of water before meals.

Important: Diet soda isn't a good substitute for water—the artificial sweeteners that are used increase sugar cravings and slow metabolism. Studies have found a 67% increase in diabetes risk in people who use artificial sweeteners.

Mark Hyman, MD, founder and medical director of The UltraWellness Center in Lenox, Massachusetts, *www.DrHyman.com*. He also is author of several books, including *The Blood Sugar Solution: The UltraHealthy Program for Losing Weight, Preventing Disease, and Feeling Great Now!* (Little, Brown).

REPORT #42

Health Secrets of the World's Longest-Living People

The residents of Okinawa, a chain of islands in Japan, are among the healthiest and longest-lived people in the world. Okinawa has more 100-year-olds than anywhere else—33.6 per 100,000 people, compared with approximately 10 per 100,000 in the United States. *The 25-year Okinawa Centenarian Study discovered that, compared with Americans, Okinawans have...*

- **80% lower risk of breast and prostate cancers.**
- **50% lower risk of colon and ovarian cancers.**
- **40% fewer hip fractures.**
- **Minimal risk of heart disease.**

What is the secret to the Okinawans' longevity—and what can we do to get the same healthful vigor? *See below...*

Accepting Attitude

While many Americans have Type A personalities, Okinawans believe that life's travails will work themselves out. They don't ignore stress...but they rarely internalize it. Stress signals your body to secrete large amounts of cortisol and other stress hormones. That damages the heart and blood vessels and accelerates bone loss.

To reduce stress: Don't take on more than you can handle ... take advantage of flextime at work...don't get uptight over things you can't change...do deep breathing and meditation.

Low-Calorie Intake

Okinawans consume an average of 1,900 calories a day, compared with 2,500 for Americans.

Reason: Harmful oxygen molecules (free radicals) are created every time the body metabolizes food for energy. Because the Okinawans take in fewer calories, their lifetime exposure to free radicals—which damage cells in the arteries, brain and other parts of the body—is reduced.

Plant-Based Diet

About 98% of the traditional Okinawan diet consists of sweet potatoes, soy-based foods, grains, fruits and vegetables. This is supplemented by a small amount of fish (or lean pork on special occasions). These plant foods contain phytonutrients—chemical compounds that reduce free radical damage. A plant-based diet is also high in fiber, which lowers cholesterol and reduces the risk of diabetes, breast cancer and heart disease.

Fish

Fish harvested from the waters surrounding Okinawa is an integral part of the daily diet. The omega-3 fatty acids in fish "thin" the blood and reduce the risk of clots—the main cause of heart attack. Americans can get similar benefits by eating fish at least three times a week. Cold-water fish—salmon, mackerel, tuna—contain the largest amounts of omega-3s. Fish oil supplements are a worthwhile alternative for people who are "fish phobic."

Jasmine Tea

Okinawans drink about three cups of jasmine tea daily. It contains more antioxidant flavonoids than black tea. Those antioxidants may reduce risk for heart disease as well as some cancers.

Not Smoking

In the US, hundreds of thousands of people die from smoking-related diseases every year. Few elderly Okinawans have ever smoked.

Exercise

People are healthiest when they combine aerobic, strengthening and flexibility exercises. Okinawans often get all three by practicing martial arts or a traditional style of dance.

Spirituality and Religion

People who have strong spiritual or religious beliefs live longer than those who do not. Spirituality and religion are a part of daily life in Okinawa. People pray daily for health and peace. They look out for one another in a "help thy neighbor" ethic called Yuimaru. Moderation is a key cultural value.

Bradley J. Willcox, MD, physician-investigator in geriatrics Okinawa Centenarian Study and associate clinical professor of geriatric medicine, University of Hawaii, both in Honolulu.

***

REPORT #43

The Little Pill That Will Save Your Life

Until recently, physicians seldom diagnosed deficiencies of vitamin D except in occasional cases of childhood rickets (a disease in which the bones do not harden).

Now: One in three Americans is considered to be deficient in vitamin D—and most of them don't even know it, according to the US National Center for Health Statistics. What should be done about it?

New Discoveries

To produce adequate levels of vitamin D naturally, you need to expose your skin (without sunscreen) to ultraviolet B (UVB) rays from sunshine for about 15 minutes, as a general guideline, twice every week. If you use sunscreen, your body makes little or no vitamin D. And, UVB rays don't pass through glass, so sitting in a sunny window will not produce vitamin D. An overwhelming body of evidence shows that vitamin D not only affects bone health (by facilitating the absorption of calcium), but also may play a main role in combatting a wide variety of ailments that include cardiovascular disease...autoimmune conditions (rheumatoid arthritis, lupus and multiple sclerosis)...chronic bone or muscle pain (including back pain)... macular degeneration...and increased colds and flu. A number of studies also have shown a link between adequate blood levels of vitamin D and lowerrisk for some types of cancer, including colon, lung, breast and prostate cancers as well as Hodgkin's lymphoma (cancer of the lymphatic system).

Important recent finding: In one study of 13,000 initially healthy men and women, the researchers at Johns Hopkins found that vitamin D deficiency was associated with a 26% increase in death from any cause during a median period of nine years.

How Vitamin D Helps

Recent scientific discoveries have demonstrated that vitamin D is critical for the health of every organ in the body. By acting as a signaling molecule, vitamin D helps cells "talk" to each other, which in turn helps control how they behave. Cellular communication is essential for healthy biology.

Without enough vitamin D, your body may continue to function, but it is more likely to experience a breakdown of cellular communication that can lead to the conditions described above.

Are You at Risk?

Deficiency of vitamin D can occur without any obvious signs. When symptoms do occur, muscle weakness and musculoskeletal pain are the common symptoms.

Frightening recent study: People with a severe vitamin D deficiency were more than two times as likely to die of heart disease and other causes than people with normal levels of vitamin D.

Among those at greatest risk for a vitamin D deficiency...

• **People over age 50.** Skin progressively loses some of its ability to convert sunlight to the active form of vitamin D.

• **People who have dark skin (anyone who is of non-European ancestry).** Dark skin pigmentation offers some protection from skin cancer because it reduces the sun's cancer-causing UVB rays. But, we need these rays to produce vitamin D.

• **People who have limited exposure to sun.** Those who live in most parts of the US, except the extreme South, do not produce sufficient vitamin D from sun exposure in the winter months. Elderly people who may spend less time outdoors also are at increased risk for vitamin D deficiency.

Avoiding a Deficiency

Many doctors now advise their patients to receive a blood test that measures levels of 25-hydroxy—a form of vitamin D that acts as a marker for vitamin D deficiency. If you are concerned about your vitamin D levels, ask your primary care physician for the test—it typically costs $50 to $100 and is covered by some health insurers.

My recommendation: Get the test in the winter. If done in the summer, when you are likely to get more sun exposure, the test may reflect higher vitamin D levels than is typical for you at other times of the year. The medical experts have increased the recommended blood levels for vitamin D—levels of 30 nanograms per milliliter (ng/ mL) are considered adequate—but a more desirable range for most people is 31 ng/mL to 90 ng/mL. The US adequate intake level for vitamin D (from food and/ or supplements) is 600 international units (IU) every day for adults under age 70 and 800 IU for adults age 70 and older. However, the consensus among researchers of vitamin D is that most adults should be taking vitamin D supplements totaling 1,000 IU daily…and 2,000 IU daily might be even better. Ask your doctor what the right dosage is for you. Either dosage can be taken along with a multivitamin. It is nearly impossible to get enough vitamin D from diet alone. In the US, milk and other dairy products and several breakfast cereals are fortified with vitamin D. Other sources such as salmon, sardines, egg yolks and beef liver also provide small amounts. To get 1,000 IU of vitamin D per day from food, you would need to consume about 10 cups of vitamin D–fortified milk or orange juice…eat 30 sardines…oreat 55 egg yolks.

Helpful : When looking to buy your vitamin D supplement, check for *vitamin D3* (cholecalciferol). This is twice as potent as *vitamin D2* (ergocalciferol).

Caution: Because vitamin D is fat-soluble, consuming more than 10,000 IU daily (or 70,000 IU weekly) can lead to toxic reactions, such as weakness, nausea and vomiting.

Reinhold Vieth, PhD, a professor in the department of nutritional sciences and the department of laboratory medicine and pathobiology at Mount Sinai Hospital, University of Toronto, Canada. He is also director of the bone and mineral laboratory. Dr. Vieth has studied vitamin D for more than 30 years and has written more than 70 related professional articles.

REPORT #44

Tattoos? Why You Must Tell Your Doctor Before an MRI

Anything that contains metal may cause a burn during magnetic resonance imaging (MRI), and permanent tattoos sometimes are done using ink that contains iron oxide. If you have a tattoo, talk to your doctor before an MRI.

Other things that contain metal and should be removed before an MRI: Body piercings, hearing aids, removable dental work, medication patches and makeup that contains metallic particles.

Health After 50. *www.JohnsHopkinsHealthAlerts.com/health_after_50*

REPORT #45

Medical Conditions Doctors Misdiagnose

Every year in the US, an estimated 40,000 to 80,000 hospital deaths are caused by diagnostic errors, according to a report in *The Journal of the American Medical Association*. When researchers use autopsies to discover discrepancies between diagnosed and actual causes of deaths, the error rate can be as high as 40%.

Conditions often misdiagnosed…

• **Alzheimer's disease.** It is impossible to diagnose this condition with 100% certainty because the only definitive "test" is an autopsy of the patient's brain after death. Even though there are fairly accurate ways to determine that a patient might have Alzheimer's (see below), mistakes are common.

Examples: Depression is one of the most common causes of Alzheimer's-like symptoms, but doctors often fail to recognize it. Other problems, including nutritional deficiencies and medication side effects—for example, from anticholinergic drugs, such as antihistamines, incontinence medications and tricyclic antidepressants—also can cause symptoms that mimic Alzheimer's.

Surprising fact: It's estimated that 10% to 25% of patients with symptoms of dementia (such as memory problems and/or peculiar behavior) may have a non-Alzheimer's condition that could be reversed with the proper treatment.

What to do: Don't accept a diagnosis of Alzheimer's disease after a single office visit or after taking a simple questionnaire. Specialists (such as neurologists) take a very detailed personal and family history…conduct neurological and mental-status tests…and order a variety of blood and imaging tests to determine whether other conditions might be involved.

• **Deep vein thrombosis (DVT).** A blood clot anywhere in the vascular system can be deadly. Those that form in the deep veins in the legs are particularly risky because the symptoms—if there are any—can seem minor. For that reason, some people don't even seek medical care, or doctors may assume that the symptoms are caused by a leg strain or sprain.

The risk: A clot can break free and enter a lung, creating a deadly pulmonary embolism. About 20% of DVT patients who develop pulmonary embolism will die from it.

What to do: If you have leg pain, leg cramps or a sense of tightness in one leg that you can't explain (discomfort in both legs probably is not caused by DVT), speak to your doctor right away. If he/she is unavailable, go to an urgent-care center or hospital emergency department. It's particularly important that you get medical attention if you have DVT symptoms and are at increased risk for the condition due to cardiovascular risk factors, such as smoking or high blood pressure.

You are also at higher risk for DVT for at least three months after knee/hip replacement or if you've recently been immobile for hours at a time, as may occur on a long airplane flight. Other DVT symptoms may include swelling, tenderness or a reddish or bluish tint on part of the leg. DVT is easy to diagnose with an ultrasound or a CT or MRI scan.

Important: Call 911 if you experience any symptoms of pulmonary embolism—such as sudden shortness of breath or sudden, sharp chest pain that may worsen when you breathe deeply or cough.

• **Hypothyroidism.** Patients who produce too little thyroid hormone (hypothyroidism) may have the condition for years before it is diagnosed because the symptoms are usually vague and seemingly minor.

Common scenario: A doctor might assume that a patient who complains of fatigue, recent weight gain or apathy is suffering from stress or depression and write a prescription for an antidepressant.

What to do: Insist on a blood test to check your thyroid hormone levels if you have any of the above symptoms. Fatigue that's accompanied by an increased sensitivity to cold often is a sign of hypothyroidism. So is hair loss (but not that due to male-pattern baldness). For unknown reasons, thinning of the outer one-third of the eyebrows is also a red flag for hypothyroidism.

Experts disagree on the optimal range for thyroid stimulating hormone (TSH). Current guidelines suggest that it should fall somewhere between 0.45 milli-international units per liter (mIU/L) and 4.49 mIU/L. (The specific values will depend on the laboratory that your doctor uses.) If your TSH is normal but symptoms persist, ask your doctor about other blood tests, such as free T3/T4 or anti-thyroglobulin. In some patients, these tests are useful in detecting hypothyroidism.

Most people do well with a thyroid replacement regimen. Some will benefit from *levothyroxine* (Levoxyl, Levothroid, Synthroid, etc.), while others find that natural desiccated thyroid hormone, such as Armour Thyroid, Nature-Throid or Westhroid, provides a better balance of T3 and T4 hormones.

Joe Graedon, MS, and Teresa Graedon, PhD, consumer advocates whose first book, *The People's Pharmacy*, was published in 1976. Since then, they have written "The People's Pharmacy" syndicated newspaper column, which discusses various issues related to drugs, herbs and vitamins. Their most recent book is *Top Screwups Doctors Make and How to Avoid Them* (Harmony). *www.PeoplesPharmacy.com*

REPORT #46

Dental X-Ray Danger

Does your dentist take X-rays every time you get a checkup? If so, there's a recent study that you should know about.

Researchers from Yale and Brigham and Women's Hospital found that people (mean age 57) who received "bitewing" exams (using X-ray film held in place by a tab between the teeth) yearly or more frequently over their lifetimes were 50% more likely than a control group to develop a meningioma, a noncancerous brain tumor that can cause headaches, vision problems and loss of speech, during a five-year period. People who had been given "panorex" exams (X-rays that show all of the teeth on one film) one or more times a year had triple the risk.

It is true that modern dental X-rays use less radiation than in the past, but any exposure is risky.

"I go to the dentist two or three times a year, but haven't had an X-ray in probably 10 years," says Keith Black, MD, chairman of the department of neurosurgery at Cedars-Sinai Medical Center in Los Angeles. *Dr. Black's advice...*

• **Refuse "routine" X-rays.** If your dentist has examined your teeth and deemed them healthy, don't allow him/her to take an X-ray "just to be safe." Risk for a brain tumor increases with every X-ray.

• **Limit the exposure.** If you have a cavity or other problems, ask your dentist to X-ray only that area.

• **Less is more.** The American Dental Association recommends that adults get their teeth X-rayed every two to three years (children—one X-ray every one to two years). Unless your dentist needs to evaluate a specific problem or plan a procedure, you don't need an X-ray.

Rebecca Shannonhouse, editor, *Bottom Line/Health*, 281 Tresser Blvd., Stamford, Connecticut 06901. *www.BottomLineHealth.com*

When Cholesterol Won't Go Down

Almost all of the estimated 42 million Americans with high cholesterol can lower it with diet and exercise—or, when necessary, with statin medicine or other cholesterol-lowering drugs. But what do you do if your cholesterol levels do not improve substantially with standard therapies? About one in every 500 Americans has an inherited predisposition to high cholesterol—a condition known as familial hypercholesterolemia (FH), which is marked by LDL "bad" cholesterol levels ranging from 150 milligrams per deciliter (mg/dL) to 1,000 mg/dL. Dietary changes may have some positive effect on patients with FH but typically do not decrease LDL levels to a normal range. Cholesterol-lowering medicine is sometimes sufficient for people with FH—but not always.

Skyrocketing LDL

Most doctors diagnose FH based on very high levels of LDL and the presence of fatty deposits on certain parts of the body.

Important red flag: Xanthomas (deposits of cholesterol). These occur most often in the Achilles tendons, but also over the knuckles, elbows, knees and bottom of the feet. They're most commonly seen in people with FH who have LDL levels above 200 mg/dL. If you have these, see a doctor for an evaluation.

Medication

Most people with FH can reach normal—or nearly normal—cholesterol levels with medication. Typically, more potent statins are prescribed at the upper end of the dose range.

The good news about side effects: Even though statin related side effects, such as muscle pain, are more likely to occur when high doses are used, people with FH who take such doses of these drugs do not appear to have more side effects than individuals without FH who take lower doses. Most patients with FH require combination therapy—treatment with a statin plus one or more additional cholesterollowering drugs, like *ezetimibe* (Zetia)...bile-acid resins, such as cholestyramine...or high-dose niacin.

"Dialysis" For LDL

A procedure, known as LDL apheresis, filters LDL from the blood, similar to the way dialysis filters toxins from the blood when the kidneys are not able to do so. LDL apheresis can decrease LDL levels by at least 50% and sometimes by as much as 75%.

How it works: At an outpatient clinic, a needle attached to a catheter is inserted into a vein in the arm. Over a period of about 90 minutes, up to three quarts of blood are withdrawn from the body and passed through a series of filters that remove the LDL. The "cleansed" blood then gets returned to the body through another vein.

Who can benefit: LDL apheresis is recommended for patients who do not have atherosclerotic cardiovascular disease and whose LDL levels are 300 mg/dL or above and who can't significantly lower their LDL after maximum therapy, including medication. Additionally, if you have been diagnosed with atherosclerotic cardiovascular disease and your LDL level is 200 mg/dL or above after maximum treatment, you may benefit from LDL apheresis. Patients with cardiovascular disease whose LDL levels are above 200 mg/dL and who cannot tolerate the side effects of statins also are eligible. The results from apheresis are immediate. Cholesterol levels are tested before and after the procedure. It is not uncommon for LDL to drop from greater than 300 mg/dL to as low as 35 mg/dL. Apheresis can also reduce C-reactive protein and fibrinogen, substances that increase risk for blood clots.

Not a cure: Apheresis does not eliminate the underlying genetic problem in people with FH, so LDL rises after the procedure. LDL apheresis patients must repeat the treatment every two weeks, possibly for the rest of their lives. LDL apheresis is very safe. There is a potential risk for unwanted bleeding (both internally or from the needle site) because the blood thinner heparin is used to keep blood flowing during the procedure. But, this type of bleeding rarely occurs. Patients who have LDL apheresis often report reduction in cardiovascular symptoms as well as lower cholesterol. Apheresis is currently offered at more than 40 medical centers across the US. Each treatment costs $2,500 to $3,000 and is covered by Medicare and most insurance plans.

Anne Carol Goldberg, MD, an associate professor of medicine in the division of endocrinology, metabolism and lipid research at the Washington University School of Medicine in St. Louis.

REPORT #48

Delicious Heart-Healthy Foods

Many people believe that managing cholesterol is key to preventing heart disease. That's not necessarily so. *Here are six common misconceptions...*

Not true: Most heart attack patients have high cholesterol.

About half of heart attack patients turn out to have perfectly normal cholesterol. When Harvard researchers analyzed data from the Nurses' Health Study, they found that about 82% of heart attacks and other "coronary events" were linked to smoking, excessive alcohol consumption, obesity, a lack of exercise and poor diet—not high cholesterol.

Not true: All LDL "bad" cholesterol is dangerous.

Some forms of LDL are harmful, but others are not. The standard cholesterol test doesn't make this distinction. You can have sky-high LDL with a low risk for heart disease. Conversely, even if your LDL is low, your risk for heart disease could be high.

Scientists have identified several subtypes of LDL that act in totally different ways. For example, subtype A is a large, pillowy molecule that does not cause atherosclerosis, the underlying cause of most heart attacks. Subtype B, a small, dense molecule, is dangerous because it is prone to oxidation and can penetrate artery walls, one of the first steps in heart disease.

What to do: Ask your doctor for an expanded cholesterol test. It will measure the different types of LDL particles and the number of particles as well as triglycerides, HDL and other substances. The test probably won't be covered by insurance, but it's reasonably priced—usually around $100.*

Not true: Cholesterol should be as low as possible.

It doesn't matter if your total cholesterol is above or below 200 milligrams per deciliter (mg/dL). What matters is your size pattern, the ratio of small-to-large LDL molecules.

Suppose your LDL is high, with a large concentration of fluffy, subtype-A particles. This is known as Pattern A. Your cholesterol-associated risk for heart disease is negligible.

You do have to worry if you have Pattern B. It means that you have a lot of the artery-damaging subtype-B particles and that your risk for heart disease is elevated. The expanded cholesterol test can help determine this.

Not true: You need a statin if you have high LDL.

The statin medications, such as *simvastatin* (Zocor) and *atorvastatin* (Lipitor), can help some patients with high LDL. If your LDL is Pattern B, a statin could save your life. You probably don't

*Price subject to change.

need a statin, or any other cholesterol-lowering drug, if you have Pattern A.

There's good evidence that statins are effective for secondary prevention—they help prevent subsequent heart attacks in patients (especially middle-aged men) who already have had a heart attack. This is not because of a cholesterol-lowering effect but because statins stabilize plaque, thin the blood and are anti-inflammatory.

Overall, however, statins don't do much for primary prevention (preventing a heart attack in patients who do not have existing heart disease).

If you're generally healthy and your only "symptom" is high cholesterol, you probably don't need a statin or any other cholesterol-lowering drug.

Not true: Saturated fat is dangerous.

Forget what you've heard—the saturated fat in red meat, butter and eggs does not increase your risk for heart disease.

Researchers from Harvard and other institutions analyzed 21 previous studies that looked at the relationship between saturated fat and heart disease. Their meta-analysis included nearly 350,000 subjects who were followed for between five and 23 years.

Conclusion: Saturated fat did not cause an increase in heart disease or stroke.

Not true: Carbohydrates are healthier than fats.

The conventional advice to substitute carbohydrates for dietary fat is misguided—and dangerous.

A Harvard study compared the progression of heart disease in postmenopausal women who changed their intakes of certain foods, including carbohydrates and saturated fat. Researchers found that women who consumed more saturated fat had less disease progression. Those who ate more carbohydrates got worse.

Another study found that the risk for a heart attack was higher in patients who replaced saturated fat with refined carbohydrates.

Not all carbohydrates are bad. People who eat healthy carbs— such as whole grains, legumes and vegetables—will probably do better, regardless of their fat intake. What people tend to consume, however, is refined carbohydrates—white bread, white rice, desserts.

Sugar is particularly bad because it increases arterial inflammation, insulin levels and blood pressure. It also elevates triglycerides, one of the main heart disease risk factors.

What helps: The best ways to reduce your risk for heart disease include maintaining a healthy weight, exercising regularly and not smoking.

Jonny Bowden, PhD, CNS, a nutritionist and nationally known expert on weight loss, nutrition and health. Based in Los Angeles, he is board-certified by the American College of Nutrition and a member of the American Society of Nutrition. *www.JonnyBowden.com*

REPORT #49

The Greatest Weight-Loss Secret No One Ever Told You

The Shangri-la Diet (named after the mythical utopia) is a very simple, effective way to adjust your natural appetite regulation system.

How this works: Much like a thermostat maintains your house temperature at a set level, your body maintains a set point weight—the number it perceives as normal. Just as a thermostat turns a heater on and off, your body's weight-control system turns hunger on and off. If the set point is adjusted upward, your body tries to put on weight...and if the set point is adjusted downward, you naturally lose weight.

Theory: Your body regulates weight partly in response to the flavors of food. A food whose flavor is associated with calories raises your set point and increases your appetite later...a flavorless food lowers your set point and curbs appetite.

Typical result: Two 100-calorie doses of flavorless foods reduce your appetite so much that the next day you automatically consume 500 fewer calories than usual—without feeling hungry.

What works best...

• **Flavorless oil.** Choose extra-light olive oil or refined walnut oil. One dose equals one tablespoon.

• **Sugar water.** Strangely, your body doesn't count sweetness as a flavor. One dose equals two tablespoons of sugar mixed with one cup of water.

Daily doses: To lose less than 20 pounds, consume one dose each of oil and sugar water daily. To lose more, double each dose. Appetite suppression usually begins within a day or so.

Essential: To prevent flavorless foods from becoming associated with other flavors, you must wait one hour after tasting anything else (including toothpaste or gum) before swallowing the oil or sugar water—then wait one hour more before eating again. Otherwise, the flavorless foods simply add to your total calorie intake without suppressing appetite at all.

Convenient: Schedule food-free intervals for mid-morning (between breakfast and lunch) and bedtime.

Troubleshooting: If swallowing pure oil makes you gag, mix the oil with the sugar water, then divide into two doses. If you develop diarrhea, cut your oil dose in half for a few days. *If you have...*

- **Gallbladder problems**—take just one teaspoon of oil per dose...or use only the sugar water.

- **Diabetes and/or recurrent yeast infections**—use only the oil.

Achieving your goal: Typically, people lose one to two pounds per week. Once you reach your target weight, reduce your dose of oil and/or sugar water to a level that allows you to maintain your weight loss. Do not stop altogether, or you may regain the weight.

The late Seth Roberts, PhD, was a professor emeritus of psychology at University of California, Berkeley, and professor of psychology at Tsinghua University in Beijing,China. Dr. Roberts was author of *The Shangri-La Diet: The No Hunger, Eat Anything Weight-Loss Plan* (Perigee) and served on the editorial board of the journal *Nutrition.*

REPORT #50

The Non-Surgical Facelift

In recent years, the science of reducing wrinkles has been transformed by the introduction of remarkable new devices and treatments that don't involve surgery. There are several developments that could help both men and women to look and feel better if they are concerned about wrinkles. *Here are the latest innovations...*

• **Digital imaging machine that provides a computerized analysis of your skin.** A device called Visia, made by Canfield Clinical Systems, uses a computer-aided digital camera to analyze the facial skin in minute detail. It gives doctors an unprecedented ability to diagnose skin conditions and monitor the effectiveness of various treatments. Visia is now becoming widely available.

How it works: With the patient's head immobilized, digital photographs are taken under different types of light to identify the specific location and depth of various skin features, including wrinkles, brown spots, enlarged pores and acne. An ultraviolet light is used to scan for latent sun damage, which will emerge as the patient gets older. When the analysis is complete, the patient's profile is matched against a database containing thousands of profiles. A percentile score shows how the patient's skin compares with that of people of similar age, gender and skin type. This analysis can then be used to guide doctors in prescribing and administering treatments. On subsequent visits, new digital images are taken to measure how well the skin is responding.

• **Laser treatment that stimulates skin to renew itself.** Intense pulsed light (IPL) photorejuvenation is becoming the treatment of choice for eliminating fine wrinkles, brown spots, broken capillaries and birthmarks—all without any recovery time.

How it works: This treatment produces light pulses at a variety of wavelengths, which penetrate the skin to different depths, depending on the problem being treated (brown spots tend to lie near the surface, for example, while broken capillaries are slightly below). This allows blemishes to be treated precisely without damaging surrounding tissue. Even better, IPL can penetrate below the top layer of skin (epidermis) to stimulate the cells that produce collagen and elastin—naturally occurring tissues that make skin more firm and elastic, and which we tend to lose as we get older. IPL photorejuvenation reverses this aging effect, making skin tighter and plumper. While IPL has been around for a number of years, a newer machine called the Lumenis One (manufactured by Lumenis) represents a significant advance over previous IPL devices. This treatment is available in most states. For more, call 877-586-3647 or go to *www.aesthetic.lumenis.com*. Sessions last about 20 minutes. Typically, patients undergo a series of IPL treatments over several weeks, followed up by a maintenance treatment every six months. With the older IPL technology, treatments lasted for 45 minutes, but the maintenance intervals were the same as for the new technology.

Cost: $200 to $500 per treatment.

• **Radio frequency devices** that use radio frequency to tighten up the skin have been available to individuals for years, but the device known as Titan (manufactured by Cutera) represents a huge improvement over all previous machines. It is safer, more effective and less expensive. It is available throughout the US and abroad. Radio frequency devices operate in the infrared range to heat the tissue under the skin surface, causing loose skin and its underlying collagen to contract and tighten. The treatment is effective even on large wrinkles. Since it doesn't remove any layers of skin, there is no flaking or redness following the treatment, eliminating the need for recovery time. Radio frequency treatment is FDA approved for use on the forehead and around the eyes and for other areas. A series of treatments may be needed for optimal results. It is not yet known how long results last.

Cost: $250 to $2,000 a treatment, depending on the area covered and amount of time involved.

• **Hyaluronic filler that replaces collagen.** Deeper lines can be temporarily eliminated by injecting a filler material into the fat layer directly beneath the depressed area. Until 2003, the only filler approved for use in the US was bovine collagen, derived from cattle. Injections of collagen will last about three months and require allergy testing before use.

In December 2003, the FDA approved Restylane, a hyaluronic acid product already available in some 60 countries. Since hyaluronic acid occurs naturally in humans (it's the material between your cells), it's nonallergenic, and no skin test is needed. Restylane injections also last much longer than collagen injections—typically up to a year. Many dermatologists and aesthetic surgeons now use Restylane exclusively, while others continue to offer both Restylane and collagen.

Cost: $400 to $1,500 per treatment.

Multi-treatment skin maintenance: Taking advantage of the array of new tools described above, many people are now adopting a maintenance program where they visit a physician (either a plastic surgeon, dermatologist or other medical doctor who has been trained to perform aesthetic services) every six months for IPL treatment and Botox injections, and on every second visit, once a year, they receive a Restylane touch-up. To find such a physician, visit *www.obagi.com*.)

Bottom line: Women and men who follow this innovative skin rejuvenation program not only have great-looking skin, but also have at their disposal a less-invasive alternative to cosmetic surgery as they get older.

Barry DiBernardo, MD, board-certified plastic surgeon and past president of the New Jersey Society of Plastic Surgeons. He is director of New Jersey Plastic Surgery, a private practice in Montclair, New Jersey.

REPORT #51

Natural Remedies for Younger Skin

I t's a fact of life that our skin becomes more wrinkled as we age. But you may be surprised to learn that our skin starts changing as early as age 30 for both women and men.

What happens: The cells that make up the skin divide more slowly with age, so the top layer of skin gets about 10% thinner every decade. The result? You guessed it—more wrinkles as well as more bruises...uneven skin tone...and sagging skin. Of course, you can "refresh" your appearance with Botox and skin fillers, but even "inexpensive" cosmetic procedures cost hundreds of dollars.

A better option: Natural skin care. Used properly, natural approaches can take years off your appearance.

Step 1: Tweak Your Diet

While you might think that skin-care products are the logical choice to smooth wrinkled skin, it's wise to first work from the "inside out" to give your skin the nutrients it needs to look its best.

Increasing laboratory evidence and positive reports from patients suggest that the following foods promote younger-looking skin...

• **High-sulfur foods.** Sulfur is known to be one of the "building blocks" of collagen, a protein that strengthens skin and gives it elasticity. Fortunately, sulfur is found in a number of foods.

My advice: At least once a day, eat sulfur-rich foods.

Good choices: Eggs, chives, legumes (such as black, white or kidney beans) and fish that is high in omega-3 fatty acids (such as salmon and sardines).

• **Grape juice or red wine.** These contain flavonoids known as proanthocyanidins and proteins called tenascins—both help make the skin smoother and more elastic.

My advice: Enjoy a daily glass of grape juice—or red wine if your doctor says daily alcohol consumption is appropriate for you. Both are high in proanthocyanidins.

In addition, a grape seed extract supplement (typical dose 200 mg once a day) is beneficial, but check first with your doctor if you take medication, especially a blood thinner—the supplement may interact with certain drugs.

• **Soy foods.** Tofu, soy milk and other foods derived from soy can make skin appear significantly younger. This is mainly due to genistein, an antioxidant in soy that slows skin aging and increases collagen.

My advice: Have one or more daily servings of soy foods.

Good choices: Edamame (steamed soy beans) and miso (a fermented paste used in cooking). Check first with your doctor if you have breast cancer or kidney disease or take any medication. Soy may be harmful for some breast cancer and kidney disease patients...it may also interact with certain drugs, including blood thinners and some antidepressants.

Also: To help keep skin hydrated, drink eight eight-ounce glasses of water each day.

Step 2: Use the Right Skin-Care Products

Skin-care products can help smooth wrinkles and provide other benefits, but there are so many on the market that most people are confused about which to use. *Best choices for younger-looking skin...*

• **Topical vitamin C.** About 80% of the dermis (the second layer of skin) consists of that all important protein collagen. Because collagen production declines with age, it's a good idea to promote collagen production any way you can.

That's where vitamin C enters the picture. The body uses vitamin C to produce collagen, but whatever is consumed orally doesn't reach adequate concentrations in the skin to boost collagen. That's why you need to apply it topically.

My advice: Use skin-care products (such as lotions and sunscreens) that have ascorbic acid (vitamin C)—the best form of the vitamin for absorption as well as collagen production and sun protection. Studies show that topical vitamin C can reduce the appearance of fine lines and wrinkles in as little as three months.

To save money: Buy powdered vitamin C at a health-food store, and mix in a small pinch each time you use a moisturizer/sunscreen that does not contain the vitamin.

• **Retinoic acid.** This is a form of vitamin A that is added to hundreds of over-the-counter (OTC) skin-care products. It is also available by prescription. Retinoic acid increases cellular turnover, the rate at which cells divide. This makes the skin appear brighter, smoother and plumper.

My advice: Use OTC retinol cream once daily. Apply it at night because it temporarily increases the skin's sensitivity to sun. Most products have a concentration of 1% or less. Prescription-strength retinoic acid usually is not necessary.

• **Moisturizer.** Everyone should use this as they age. Adding moisture to skin cells makes them expand, which improves skin volume and texture. Moisturizers protect the skin from environmental factors (heat, dryness and pollution) that undermine skin health.

My advice: Use moisturizer with sunscreen at least twice a day. I advise a vitamin C–enhanced moisturizer that includes green-tea extract. Both ingredients improve the skin's ability to absorb the moisturizer. Compounds in green tea also reduce skin inflammation and sun-related skin damage. Soy moisturizers may provide similar benefits.

Also important: Exfoliation, an effective form of controlled trauma that stimulates the skin to produce more collagen. Every week or two, use a gentle facial scrub with fine grains and a soft facial brush. This practice also removes the dead skin cells that dull your complexion.

Sensitive skin sometimes cannot tolerate even a mild scrub. An ultrasonic brush, such as Clarisonic ($100 to $200 at department stores and online), with a hydrating cleanser is a good alternative.

A chemical peel once or twice a year is another good way to remove dead skin cells. OTC peels contain glycolic acid, lactic acid or salicylic acid, usually in a concentration of about 5% to 10%. Peels should also contain moisturizing ingredients to minimize irritation. If you're new to chemical peels, talk with your dermatologist before using one of these products, since they can irritate skin, especially sensitive skin.

Eudene Harry, MD, medical director of Oasis for Optimal Health in Orlando, Florida. She is board-certified in both emergency and holistic medicine and serves as medical director for the Women's Wellness Society, a national group that focuses on women's health. She is the author of *Live Younger in 8 Simple Steps: A Practical Guide to Slowing Down the Aging Process from the Inside Out* (Harry). *DrHarryMD.com*

REPORT #52

Cure Baldness Naturally

The average adult scalp contains an estimated 100,000 hair follicles and loses approximately 100 hairs a day. Normally, they're replaced in five or six weeks. New hair sprouts out of tiny, tube-shaped follicles in the scalp. The most common type of hair loss is androgenic alopecia. This male (or female) pattern hair loss causes hair to grow back thinner (less hair on the scalp) or finer (each individual hair is thinner). Or it doesn't grow back at all.

How can you slow, stop or even reverse hair loss? *Minoxidil* (Rogaine), the topical treatment for men and women, is available in both prescription and over-the-counter (OTC) strengths. Dermatologists who prescribe minoxidil typically find that one-third of patients who use it have some new hair growth…one-third find their hair loss slows or stops…and one-third do not have any improvement. It can cause a rash on your scalp, costs $50 a month and must be used indefinitely. Men can take the oral prescription medication *finasteride* (Propecia), a synthetic hormone that blocks the formation of DHT. But this drug can inhibit erections and sex drive. In addition, there are hundreds of OTC treatments which promise—but fail to deliver—miraculous results.

Natural Treatments

Several natural hair-loss remedies have been shown to be effective—without causing serious side effects…

- **Saw palmetto.** This is the number-one herbal treatment of choice for androgenic alopecia in men. It works just like finasteride, blocking the formation of 5-alpha reductase, an enzyme that sparks the conversion of testosterone into DHT. But saw palmetto doesn't have the same side effects as finasteride. In fact, it may enhance sexual function. It can cause increased appetite and breast enlargement.

Typical dose: 160 milligrams (mg) daily.

Scientific evidence: In research reported in the *Journal of Alternative and Complementary Medicine*, 19 men between the ages of 23 and 64 with mild to moderate androgenic alopecia were given either saw palmetto or a placebo over five months. Of those who took the herb, 60% reported a slower rate of hair loss, more hair growth, a smaller bald spot and/or higher satisfaction with the appearance of their hair. Of those getting the placebo, only 11% reported any improvement.

- **Procyanidin B-3.** A number of studies conducted in Japan show that procyanidin—a type of flavonoid (plant pigment) extracted from barley—promotes hair growth.

Scientific evidence: In a laboratory study published in the journal *Experimental Dermatology*, researchers tested more than 1,000 plant extracts to discover which best promoted the growth of hair cells. The scientists found that procyanidin B-3 outperformed the control group by roughly 140%. Procyanidin also was found to have no side effects.

Helpful: The topical hair-loss product Revivogen, for men and women, contains both saw palmetto and procyanidin. To order, call 888-616-4247 or see *www.revivogen.com*. Crinagen, a topical spray for men, also contains both natural extracts. To order, call 727-282-1963 or go to *www.raztec.com*.

Other Types of Hair Loss

Androgenic alopecia isn't the only cause of hair loss. Thyroid disease, severe stress and side effects of medication also can lead to hair loss. In some cases, an inflammatory condition can strip the scalp of hair. Examples include irritant dermatitis (a skin reaction to a chemical in a hair product such as shampoo) and alopecia areata (an autoimmune skin disease). To combat hair loss associated with inflammation, ask your doctor about taking a daily supplement of 500 mg of *gammalinolenic acid* (GLA), an essential fatty acid found in the seeds of evening primrose, black currant and borage plants.

Important: GLA should not be taken by women who are pregnant or nursing. Because GLA has anticlotting effects, people taking *warfarin* (Coumadin) or other blood thinners, as well as hemophiliacs, should consult their doctors before taking it.

Aromatherapy

The "essential oils" of aromatherapy can increase blood flow to the scalp, which helps promote hair regrowth.

What to do: In a small, clean bottle, add one to two drops of essential oil of cayenne for every ounce of essential oil of rosemary. Lightly coat your scalp with this mixture, and massage into your scalp for 20 minutes daily. Use any shampoo to rinse.

Jeanette Jacknin, MD, board-certified dermatologist in Scottsdale, Arizona, and author of *Smart Medicine for Your Skin* (Avery).

REPORT #53

How to Find Love Again After 50

I f you were married for many years before losing a spouse to death or divorce, the prospect of dating again may seem intimidating. Yet with patience and persistence, you can find a wonderful partner—and enjoy the search in the meantime.

Common fears about dating and how to overcome them…

Fear: "I'm too old/unattractive."

Reality: Age need not be a barrier to meeting someone new—it even can be an advantage. At this stage in life, you likely have developed many sources of fulfillment aside from romance, such as an established career or hobbies that you are passionate about…as well as clarity about values and what matters most in life. Self-knowledge and the confidence it brings can make you radiant to the opposite sex.

As for attractiveness, you don't need classic good looks to appeal to the opposite sex. Health and vitality are powerful attractors. To project these qualities, get regular exercise. Walk with your spine long and your head high.

You also may want to consult an image consultant or department-store personal shopper to update your style. Whatever your body type, contemporary clothes that fit well will help you project a radiant image—and this goes for men as well as women.

Fear: "I'll put a profile on a dating Web site, and no one will be interested."

Reality: The 50+ segment is the fastest-growing group on dating Internet sites. It should be a part of everyone's dating strategy. You can take simple steps to improve your online dating success and capture the attention of interesting people. *Keys to success online…*

- **Register with more than one site.** To increase your exposure to people who might be a good fit, start with two sites. One should cast a wide net, such as Match.com or eHarmony.com. The second should be more specialized, such as JDate.com (for Jewish singles), Catholic Mingle.com (for Catholics) or OurTime.com (for people over 50).

- **Show, don't tell.** Don't post a list of interests and adjectives about yourself—everyone does that. To stand out, tell brief stories about those qualities.

Example: Instead of vague phrases such as "love to travel," describe what inspired you about your most recent trip.

Ask friends what they see as your top five characteristics and for vignettes that illustrate them. Incorporate these examples into your profile.

- **Post current photos.** Choose four or five current photos that look like you and that show you at your best. The main profile photo should be a close-up of your face. The others should show you in a variety of poses doing things that you love. If you don't have recent photos, ask a friend to take some.

- **Don't wait to be discovered.** If someone's profile interests you, send him/her a message through the site. This applies to women as well as men—it is perfectly acceptable, and expected, for women to contact men on dating sites.

- **Make your message short, catchy and specific.** Mention one or two things in the profile that made the person stand out for you, such as a warm smile, a clever turn of phrase or a book title.

Don't be discouraged or take it personally if your message doesn't receive a reply—it happens to everyone. Keep viewing profiles and contacting new people who interest you.

Fear: "I may put myself in danger."

Reality: You should take simple, sensible precautions to protect yourself…

- **Protect your privacy.** Don't use your real name as your screen name—instead, use a hobby or personality trait, such as FilmFan or LoveSailing. Have a separate e-mail address that you use only for online dating messages. Don't give out your phone number until you have built up some rapport and trust via e-mail, and use your cell phone so that the number cannot be easily traced to your home address. Choose a public place for your first few dates. Tell others where you will be. Don't get picked up or dropped off at home until you have known the person for a while.

- **Do some checking.** As soon as you know a prospect's full name—which usually is early in the e-mail stage—do an online search to determine whether he has portrayed himself accurately. In addition to searching by name, you can copy his photo into a search engine such as Google Images and perform an image search. By using this technique, I learned early on that someone I had met online had disguised his identity, made up a sob story and asked a number of women for money.

Fear: "First dates will be awkward."

Reality: First dates can be awkward, but they also can be interesting and fun. Although meeting for coffee is a classic, low-key first date, consider more active options such as visiting a museum or taking a walk downtown. Standing or walking side by side is less awkward than sitting face to face, and your surroundings will provide conversation cues.

In addition to talking about mutual interests, ask lighthearted questions that delve beneath the surface.

Examples: What would you love to do if there were no constraints? What's the best advice anyone ever gave you?

Fear: "There are a lot of losers out there."

Reality: More than any other factor, your attitude has the biggest impact on your satisfaction with dating and your ability to meet compatible people. Television and other popular media reinforce negative stereotypes of the opposite sex by portraying single men as inept or self-centered and single women as confusing or impossible to please. But these are just caricatures.

The truth: Many men are capable and loving. Many women are straightforward and agreeable.

Assess a person's character by paying attention to the person's actions as well as words. Look for evidence of kindness, respect, integrity, emotional generosity and responsibility.

Examples: Does she show up when she agreed to or keep you waiting and make excuses for being late? How does he treat the staff at a café? Does she put her cell phone away during dates and give you her full attention? When the subject of past relationships comes up, does he dwell on his ex's negative traits?

Fear: "He/she will want sex right away."

Reality: Plenty of people don't mind waiting, and someone who is right for you will respect your boundaries.

If you are interested in someone but this person is getting more physical than you are comfortable with, express your feelings frankly in a positive, nonjudgmental way.

Examples: "I'm attracted to you, but I want to slow this down"…"I don't have sex with someone this soon, so for now why don't we just kiss and cuddle."

If and when you are ready to have sex, make sure that both of you have been tested for sexually transmitted diseases. Not only is this important for your health, it also is a good gauge of your relationship. If you don't trust each other enough to show each other your test results, you're not ready to have sex.

Bottom line: The biggest obstacle to finding love in midlife or later is staying home. So move those fears aside, and get out there and date.

Sandy Weiner, dating coach, blogger and workshop leader who specializes in helping people over age 40. Based in Stamford, Connecticut, she is chief love officer at *LastFirstDate.com*, where she has posted many articles about dating in midlife. She hosts the online radio show Courageous Conversations at *www.BlogTalkRadio.com*.

3 Quick Ways to Defuse Anger

- **Sit down!** Your brain interprets a seated or reclining position as safe and relaxing, interrupting the flow of anger-enhancing adrenaline. The next time you're in an argument, get yourself (and the other person) to sit down. Say something like, "Let's sit and discuss this." If you're already sitting down when angered, try leaning back and relaxing your muscles.
- **Never go to bed angry.** Research proves that the old saying is right! A recent study found that hitting the sack after having negative emotions appears to reinforce them. Try to resolve disagreements before saying good night.
- **Become an observer.** The next time your blood boils, step back and view the situation from a distance. Evaluate how angry you are on a scale of 0 to 100. Then project what may happen if you don't lower that figure by using some of the techniques here. This will help you remain calm.

If you have extreme fight-or-flight symptoms, are getting angry more often or if others are complaining about your temper, seek professional help. Visit the American Psychological Association at *http://locator.APA.org* to find an anger-management expert.

W. Robert Nay, PhD, clinical psychologist and clinical associate professor of psychiatry at Georgetown University School of Medicine in Washington, DC. The author of *Taking Charge of Anger* (Guilford), he is in private practice in McLean, Virginia, and Annapolis, Maryland, and trains professionals in anger management. *www.WRobertNay.com*

Ancient Secret to Banishing Belly Fat and Improving Your Sex Life

About 16 million Americans regularly practice yoga for health and healing—but four out of five are women.

What few people realize: Despite its reputation as a "soft" exercise that's more suited to women, yoga can provide special health benefits for men—even helping to slow the growth of prostate cancer.

What all men need to know…*

Benefits for Men

Hundreds of scientific studies on yoga have shown that it can improve health conditions ranging from sleep problems and sinusitis to high blood pressure and schizophrenia. Many of these benefits are particularly relevant for men. *For example, yoga has been shown to…*

• **Slow prostate cancer.** In a study published in The Journal of Urology, some men with prostate cancer did 60 minutes daily of gentle yoga (stretching, breathing, meditation, guided imagery and relaxation) for one year while others did not. Those who didn't do yoga had eight times more growth of cancer cells than those who performed yoga daily.

• **Reduce abdominal fat.** Stress is behind many "spare tires," because it triggers high levels of the hormone cortisol, which stimulates appetite and overeating and then plays a key role in turning extra calories into extra belly fat. For unknown reasons, visceral fat, which releases disease-causing inflammatory chemicals, is more prevalent in men than in women.

Good news: Yoga reduces cortisol, which helps control abdominal fat.

• **Help prevent a heart attack.** Each year more than 900,000 Americans have heart attacks, and the majority of them are men.

Recent research: Yoga can reduce many of the heart attack risk factors in people who have heart disease, including high blood pressure, elevated total and LDL "bad" cholesterol and high triglycerides.

• **Improve sexual performance and satisfaction.** In a study of 65 men reported in *The Journal of Sexual Medicine*, practicing yoga an hour a day for three months improved every dimension of sexual functioning—libido…erections…ejaculatory control…satisfaction with performance, intercourse and orgasm…and sexual confidence.

*Before starting yoga, check with your doctor if you have severe osteoporosis, problems with your spine or artificial joints—you may be at greater risk for injury. Also consult your doctor if you have any chronic health conditions or recent injuries. If you develop pain, dizziness or other symptoms while doing yoga, stop the pose and tell your teacher immediately.

How to Start

Even though yoga is generally safe for most people of all ages, if you're middle-aged or older and have never practiced yoga, it's best to start with a slower, less vigorous style. *My advice...*

• **Start with a yoga class, not with a book or DVD.** Taking a class led by a skilled yoga teacher is invaluable because the teacher can look at you, review what you're doing and guide you to the best injury-free experience. Expert instruction, mindfulness and not pushing too hard during practice can prevent most injuries, such as muscle spasms and ligament strains.

Helpful: If you do use a book or DVD to learn yoga, have a skilled yoga teacher look over your routine now and then to help you correct any mistakes.

• **Find a good class for men.** Ask a male family member, friend or colleague who practices yoga for his recommendation. If you don't know any men who practice yoga, ask a woman, or visit the Web site of the International Association of Yoga Therapists, *www. IAYT.org*.

• **Don't rush results.** Men are often achievement-oriented and want fast results. That's a mistake. Yoga is not about performance or competition—it's about how the poses help you.

• **Just do it!** This is the secret to success with yoga—simply doing a yoga routine, 15 to 20 minutes a day, every day.

For overall fitness, yoga is a good complement to cardio exercise and strength training. But remember, yoga also provides stress reduction, flexibility and mental focus.

What Yoga Isn't...

Misconceptions about yoga can keep some men from trying it. Yoga is not...

• **A religion.** It is practiced by Christians, Jews, Muslims and atheists.

• **Just stretching.** Yoga includes stretching poses (asanas), as well as other techniques, such as breathing exercises and meditation.

• **A single style of exercise.** There are many styles of yoga, from slow and gentle (such as Ananda or Kripalu) to fast and vigorous (such as Power Yoga or Vinyasa Flow).

Timothy McCall, MD, a board-certified internist, medical editor of *Yoga Journal* and author of *Yoga as Medicine* (Bantam). His articles have appeared in dozens of publications, including *The New England Journal of Medicine* and *The Journal of the American Medical Association*. He teaches workshops on yoga as medicine. *www.DrMcCall.com*

You May Not Need All the Drugs You're Taking: 3 Overprescribed Medications

Nearly 60% of the prescription medications taken by patients aren't needed. That is what researchers discovered in a study published in *Archives of Internal Medicine*. The study also revealed that 88% of patients said they felt healthier when taking fewer drugs.

The fact is that adverse effects from medications are the fourth-leading cause of death in the US (after heart disease, cancer and stroke). About 6% of patients who take two medications daily will experience a drug interaction. If you're taking five medications a day, the risk rises to 50%.

As a geriatric pharmacist, I have evaluated the drug regimens of thousands of patients. *Here are the medications that often are overprescribed...*

Statins

The cholesterol-lowering statins, such as *atorvastatin* (Lipitor) and *simvastatin* (Zocor), are among the highest-selling prescription drugs in the US. They are not as effective as you might think...and the potential side effects, including muscle pain and memory loss, can be serious.

One recent study, published in *Pharmacotherapy*, found that 75% of patients who took statins reported memory loss or other cognitive problems. The same study found that 90% of patients who stopped their medication had rapid mental improvements.

Statins can be lifesaving drugs for patients who have high cholesterol and existing heart disease or other cardiovascular risk factors. But generally, they are not effective for primary prevention (preventing a heart attack in healthy patients with few risk factors).

Before starting to take a statin, ask your doctor about the drug's Number Needed to Treat (NNT). The NNT for Lipitor is 168. This means that 168 patients would have to take it (for 4.1 years) to prevent one cardiovascular event. Those are impressively bad odds, particularly when the risk for muscle pain/memory loss can be as high as one in 10.

My advice: Try to lower your cholesterol with nondrug approaches. These include taking fish-oil supplements...and eating less saturated fat and more fiber. Take a statin only if you have high cholesterol and other cardiovascular risk factors, such as a family history, high blood pressure and/or diabetes.

Painkillers

Ibuprofen and related analgesics, known as the nonsteroidal anti-inflammatory drugs (or NSAIDs), are among the most commonly utilized medications in the US. People assume they're safe. They're not.

One study found that 71% of patients who used NSAIDs experienced damage to the small intestine, compared with just 5% who didn't take them. These medications also increase the risk for stomach bleeding, ulcers and hypertension.

My advice: Take an NSAID only if you need both the painkilling and anti-inflammatory effects—for a flare-up of knee pain, for example. Take the lowest possible dose, and take it only for a few days at a time.

If you're 60 years old or older, you may need to avoid these drugs altogether. The risk for stomach or intestinal damage is much higher than in younger adults. A safer medication is *tramadol* (Ultram), a prescription analgesic that doesn't cause gastrointestinal irritation.

Sedatives

Valium and related drugs, known as benzodiazepines, are among the most dangerous medications for older adults.

Reason: They are not efficiently broken down (metabolized) in the liver. This means that high levels can accumulate in the body.

Patients who take these drugs daily for conditions such as insomnia or anxiety are 70% more likely to fall—and 50% more likely to have a hip fracture—than those who do not take them. Also, patients who use them regularly have a 50% chance of experiencing memory loss.

Sedatives such as *diazepam* (Valium), *triazolam* (Halcion) and *zolpidem* (Ambien) should never be taken for extended periods.

My advice: If you're going through a stressful time, ask your doctor to write a one- or two-week prescription for a short-acting medication such as *lorazepam* (Ativan). It is eliminated from the body more quickly than other drugs.

For long-term insomnia/anxiety, ask your doctor about *venlafaxine* (Effexor). It's good for depression as well as anxiety, and it's safer than sedatives for long-term use.

Armon B. Neel, Jr., PharmD, a certified geriatric pharmacist and founder of the Georgia-based MedicationXpert, LLC, a private practice focused on pharmaceutical care for outpatients and institutional geriatric patients. He is author of *Are Your Prescriptions Killing You? How to Prevent Dangerous Interactions, Avoid Deadly Side Effects, and Be Healthier with Fewer Drugs* (Atria). *www.MedicationXpert.com*

Quick Fixes for Aching Feet!

Anyone who has ever suffered from athlete's foot knows that antifungal creams usually clear up the condition in about two weeks. What most people don't know is that the medication must be used for a full month to eradicate the fungus. Like athlete's foot, most foot problems are either caused— or worsened—by the sufferers themselves.

Five painful foot ailments and the mistakes that cause them...

Bunions

Millions of American adults undergo surgery each year to remove bunions—bony protrusions on the outside of the big toe. Many of these surgeries could be prevented with self-care.

Common mistake: Wearing high heels or shoes with tight toes. This can cause inflammation and swelling, which irritate and worsen the bunions. To avoid this problem, it's important to buy shoes that are not too tight in the toe box. If you already suffer from bunions, you can reduce the pressure with over-the-counter orthotic inserts that support the arch. If they don't help, you may need to get prescription orthotics from a podiatrist ($250 to $500).

Wearing snug socks also reduces the friction on bunions.

To relieve painful bunion attacks: Mix up one cup of vinegar in one gallon of warm water, and soak the foot for 15 minutes daily. Also, wrap ice or a package of frozen peas in a thin towel and apply to the bunion twice a day for 15 minutes.

Calluses

Calluses are thick layers of dead skin cells that accumulate in areas of the foot exposed to frequent pressure. High heels or flat shoes can make calluses worse by shifting body weight to the fore-foot. Shoes with one-inch heels are preferable because they put less pressure on this part of the foot.

Common mistake: Using the OTC callus-removal products. They don't always work well, and the active ingredient (salicylic acid) can damage healthy skin. It is also often more effective to remove calluses after taking a warm bath or shower.

What to do: Very gently abrade the callus with a pumice stone. Before going to bed, apply a moisturizer that contains copper, a softening agent that will make calluses easier to remove. If this process doesn't help, ask your doctor about microdermabrasion. This 15- to 30-minute, painless outpatient procedure eliminates the need for surgery. During microdermabrasion, a podiatrist uses aluminum oxide crystals to exfoliate the callus.

Typical cost: $125 to $200.

Corns

These kernel-shaped areas of thickened tissue are similar to calluses but usually form at the tips of—or between—toes.

Common mistake: Cutting or roughly abrading corns. This can cause more pain and infection. Soak the corn in an Epsom salt solution for 10 minutes. Then gently rub it with a pumice stone. Repeat daily until the corn is gone.

Fallen Arches

People develop fallen arches when the feet flatten over time. This happens when aging, weight gain, excess impact from running or walking and/or hormonal changes cause loosening of the plantar fascia ligaments at the bottom of the feet. Other people may have inherited a low arch. The condition triggers arch pain—often accompanied by heel or ankle pain.

Common mistake: Forgoing physical activity. Arch pain can be reduced or eliminated with exercises that stretch the Achilles tendons and strengthen the muscles of the arch. Do each of the following stretches six times, twice per day. Hold each stretch for 30 seconds.

• **Place your right foot on a chair or step.** Keep both heels flat. Lean forward until you feel a stretch. Repeat with left foot.

• **Stand on a step facing the stairs with your feet together.** Move your right heel back until it hangs off the edge. Lower the heel until you feel a stretch in the right calf. Repeat with left foot.

• **Sit in a chair.** Rest your right ankle on your left knee. Gently pull the toes of your right foot upward toward your chest, until you feel a stretch in the arch of the foot. Repeat with the left foot.

People with fallen arches need to wear dress shoes with one-inch heels or athletic shoes with built-in arches. Slip-in orthotic inserts (prescription or OTC) are helpful as well.

To determine if you have fallen arches: Look at your footprints in wet sand. A normal foot has a gap between the heel and the forefoot. A fallen arch will have little or no gap.

Ingrown Nails

Ingrown toenails curve and push into the flesh. The condition causes pain, redness and/or swelling.

Common mistake: Trimming nails on a curve. That increases the risk for ingrown nails. To reduce risk, soak feet in warm water, wash with soap and trim nails straight across. If there is redness or other signs of infection, apply an OTC antibiotic, such as Neosporin.

If pain and redness do not go away after two days: Your doctor may need to remove the portion of nail beneath the skin. This can be done in a 15-minute outpatient procedure.

Suzanne M. Levine, DPM, podiatrist in private practice in New York City. She is author of *Your Feet Don't Have to Hurt* (St. Martin's).

6

Tax Savvy

REPORT #56

Beat the Tax Man Legally

When you retire, the paychecks stop but the taxes don't. Your income may be fixed, or nearly so, if you rely on Social Security, a pension, an annuity, etc. Meanwhile, taxes can eat up more and more of the money you need for living. *Here are ways to fight the tax hit...*

Property Taxes

For many people on modest incomes, property taxes can be higher than income taxes. *Take these steps...*

• **Apply for a senior property tax break.** Many states offer such programs. There may be income or other limitations. Contact your state's revenue (tax) department to find out what's available and how to apply.

Example: Some Illinois seniors can cut their property taxes by as much as $3,000 per year, thanks to a "senior citizen's homestead exemption."

Resource: The Federation of Tax Administrators (*www.taxadmin.org/state-tax-agencies*) has links to every state's tax authority.

• **Appeal your property assessment if you think you pay much higher taxes than your neighbors for a similar house.** If successful, you may be able to reduce your annual tax bill.

How to do it: Contact your town or county assessor's office to get the information on which it based your assessment. Look for outright mistakes about your property, such as the wrong square footage, number of bedrooms or lot size. There also may be external factors that reduce the property's value, such as heavy traffic and/or noise near your house.

Deadline alert: Each jurisdiction has an "appeal season," generally several months early in the year. Contact your jurisdiction to determine your window of opportunity.

You may be able simply to show your evidence to the county assessor to have your assessment reduced. If informal procedures don't work, go before the local assessment board to make your case.

• **Sell your house.** As long as you have owned and occupied the house for at least two of the last five years, you'll owe no tax on up to $250,000 worth of profit from the sale ($500,000 for married couples). You then can move into an apartment or buy a house with lower taxes.

If you would like to remain in your house, you can sell it to a grown son or daughter and pay him/her rent to live there. You'll pocket your tax-free gain, and, as long as you pay a fair market rent, the new owner will be entitled to the tax benefits of owning rental property—such as deductions for depreciation.

Federal Income Taxes

If your taxable income is below $50,000 and your finances are relatively straightforward, it might pay for you to take the standard deduction on IRS Form 1040EZ or Form 1040A for your federal tax return. These forms are short and simple. Otherwise, using these simple forms might lock you out of certain deductions and/or credits and cause you to overpay your taxes.

Example: If your unreimbursed medical expenses come to more than 10% (7.5% if you are 65 or older) of your adjusted gross income, you can itemize and deduct them—but only on Form 1040, the regular "long" form. *To further cut your taxes...*

- **Use borrowing power.** The IRS taxes income. Money that you borrow can provide cash flow without raising your tax bill. Use borrowed money, tax free, for some of your expenses. Today's low interest rates make such an approach practical.

Examples: You might use a home-equity line of credit with a very favorable interest rate. The interest you pay probably will be deductible if you itemize on Form 1040.

For information on home-equity interest deductibility, see IRS publication 936, Home Mortgage Interest Deduction, available from the IRS at 800-829-3676 or *www.irs.gov*.

Another possibility is to take out a loan against your cash-value life insurance or your securities portfolio.

Strategy: Keep the bulk of your long-term noncash savings in assets that do not generate much taxable income, such as growth stocks or tax-managed mutual funds.

Warning: Don't borrow at high interest rates or to excess. You might endanger your core assets—your investment portfolio, insurance policies, even your house.

- **Let your house pay you.** If you are at least 62 years old and your home is not heavily mortgaged, consider taking out a reverse mortgage. You'll get tax-free cash, and the money doesn't have to be repaid until you die or move out of the house.

Information: AARP, 888-687-2277, *www.aarp.org/revmort*.

State and Local Income Taxes

Some state and local governments provide seniors with income tax breaks that shelter pension and/or Social Security benefits. Contact your tax adviser or state tax authority. If your income is high and/or you live in an area that has high taxes even for seniors, you might want to move to a less taxing jurisdiction. Before you pick a new place to live, be sure to take all of its taxes into account. A state might have low income tax, but the area you like might have high property tax. For help comparing overall tax burdens in various states, call the Tax Foundation at 202-464-6200 or visit *www.taxfoundation.org*.

Caution: States chase down residents who try to illegally avoid taxes by claiming they've moved, perhaps by buying or renting a second home or even using a relative's address. If you move, be sure to sever your connections to your old state.

File a final income tax return with your former state, and subsequently file returns with your new state if required. Use your new address on all tax documents, and file federal returns with the IRS Service Center for your new state.

Bernie S. Kent, Esq., CPA , former managing director, Telemus Capital, 2 Towne Square, Southfield, Michigan 48076. He is past chairman of the personal financial planning committee of the Michigan Association of Certified Public Accountants.

REPORT #57

How to Earn Invisible Income The IRS Can't Touch

Not all of the money you receive is taxable income, even though the IRS might like you to think it is.

Gain on the Sale of Your Home...

You are not taxed on gain up to $250,000 ($500,000 on a joint return) from the sale of your principal residence. You qualify for this exclusion if you owned and used the home for two out of five years before the date of the sale, regardless of your age.

Life Insurance Proceeds

The beneficiary receives the proceeds of life insurance policies free of tax. However, the decedent's estate may be liable for estate tax on the proceeds.

Gifts and Inheritances

You do not pay income tax on money or property you receive as a gift or inheritance. Any gift tax owed is the responsibility of the person who gave the gift. In the case of an inheritance, federal estate tax is paid by the decedent's estate, not by the beneficiaries. If you inherit property that has increased in value, such as the family home, you receive it at its stepped-up estate value. This enables you to avoid tax on the gain. When you sell the property, you use its stepped-up value, rather than the original cost, to calculate your taxable gain—another big benefit.

Borrowed Money

You can borrow up to $50,000 from your company pension plan tax free.

Trap: If a debt you owe is canceled, the amount of debt forgiven might become taxable income to you.

Grants for Education

Scholarships and fellowship grants are tax free—provided you are a degree candidate and the money is used strictly for tuition, fees, books, supplies and required equipment. (Grants for room and board are taxable.)

Employee Awards

Awards of tangible personal property (not cash) for length of service or safety achievements—up to $400 per employee or $1,600 provided the employer has a qualified plan—are tax free. (Awards for suggestions to an employer are generally taxable.)

Damages

Any damages received in a lawsuit due to personal physical injury or sickness are tax free.

Rollovers

No taxes are payable on a lump-sum payout from a company pension plan directly transferred into an IRA or another qualified plan within 60 days.

Property Settlements

Settlements between spouses in a divorce are not taxable to the recipient. However, the recipient does take over the tax cost (basis) in the property and will be taxed on any gain when the property is sold.

Child Support and Alimony

Child-support payments are tax free to the recipient. Alimony is generally taxable, but it can be tax free if both spouses agree.

Municipal Bond Interest

Generally, the interest is exempt from federal income tax and sometimes from state and local tax as well.

Exception: Interest from certain "private activity" municipal bonds is subject to the alternative minimum tax (AMT). Also, municipal bond interest is taken into account in figuring your income level to determine whether any of your Social Security benefits are taxable.

Return-of-Capital Dividends

Some companies pay dividends that are considered a return on your investment in the company. These are wholly or partially tax free. However, your tax cost in the stock has to be reduced by the amount of untaxed dividends.

Life Insurance Policy Dividends

These are generally considered a partial return of the premiums you paid and are not taxable. You don't have to pay tax on these dividends until they exceed the accumulated premiums paid for the policy.

Annuity Payments

The part of an annuity payment that represents the return of your investment in the annuity contract is not taxed. Pension and IRA distributions that represent any non–tax-deductible contributions are also not taxed.

Education Savings Bonds

Interest on US Series EE and I savings bonds that were issued after December 31, 1989, is tax free to many taxpayers if the bonds are later redeemed to pay for education expenses.

Limits : This exclusion is not available for taxpayers with income in excess of certain annually determined amounts.

Also Tax Free

- **Workers' compensation.**
- **Social Security payments**—provided your income is less than $32,000 if married filing jointly, or $25,000 if filing singly.
- **Federal income-tax refunds.** (However, any interest the IRS pays on a late refund is taxable.)
- **State income-tax refunds,** provided that you did not itemize deductions on your federal tax return for the previous year. If, however, you itemized your deductions for the year, your state refund is taxable. State refunds are not taxable if you were subject to the AMT the previous year and got no tax benefit for your state tax payments.
- **Disability payments** from any accident or health insurance policies paid for by the taxpayer are generally not taxable. But they're usually taxable if your employer paid the premiums.
- **Foreign-earned income.** The first $100,800 of salary in 2015 earned in another country is excluded from US tax if you were a resident of that country for the entire tax year. Some of your housing expenses are also excluded from US taxes.
- **Certain fringe benefits from your employer.**

Examples: Health and accident insurance, pension plans, up to $50,000 of life insurance coverage, child- and dependent-care expenses, adoption assistance, meal money, employee discounts and transit passes not exceeding $130 per month.

- **Reimbursed medical expenses** that are not claimed as itemized deductions.
- **Reimbursed travel and entertainment expenses** that you adequately account for to your employer (unless the reimbursement is included on your W-2 form).
- **The amounts received for insurance reimbursement** up to the amount of your original cost for the damaged or lost property.

Edward Mendlowitz, CPA , partner, WithumSmith+Brown, New Brunswick, New Jersey. He is author of various books on taxes, including *The Adviser's Guide to Family Business Succession Planning* (AICPA).

Take Your Cash Now, Pay No Penalty

Anyone who withdraws money from a traditional IRA or from any other tax-deferred retirement plan will owe income tax, assuming the account was funded with deductible contributions. In most situations, you will also owe a 10% penalty tax on withdrawals before age 59½. For instance, if you withdraw $10,000 at age 54 (and don't qualify for an exception to the penalty), you would have to pay a $1,000 penalty. But there are some exceptions to the early withdrawal penalty. If you really must take an early withdrawal, use one of the following methods to avoid the 10% penalty tax bite.

Universal Exceptions

The following exceptions apply to all tax-deferred retirement plans...

• **Death.** If you inherit a retirement account, you won't face the 10% penalty. That's true no matter how old you are (and no matter how old the participant was at the time of death).

• **Disability.** Again, the 10% penalty does not apply if you cannot work and need to make a withdrawal. How can you prove to the IRS that you are disabled? In most cases, you should be receiving disability checks from Social Security or from an insurance policy.

Smart 1040 strategy: Attach an explanation to your tax return, clearly stating that you are receiving disability benefits and that the 10% penalty should not apply.

• **Medical bills.** The 10% penalty will not apply to any money spent for deductible medical expenses in excess of 10% (7.5% if you're 65 or older) of your adjusted gross income (AGI).

• **Substantially equal periodic payments (SEPPs).** Avoid the 10% penalty by withdrawing annual amounts based on your life expectancy. These payments must continue for at least five years or until age 59½, whichever comes later.

Caution: If you don't maintain the SEPPs until the later of five years or until age 59½, you will owe the 10% penalty tax on all withdrawals, retroactively.

Employer-Sponsored Plans

The following two exceptions to the 10% early withdrawal penalty apply only to withdrawals from 401(k)s, profit-sharing plans and other qualified retirement plans.

• **Separation from service.** If you leave your employer, you can take money from your retirement account and not be subject to a penalty.

Requirement: The separation must occur no earlier than the year you reach age 55.

• **Qualified domestic relations orders (QDROs).** In a divorce or marital separation, a QDRO is an order to the plan administrator to transfer a portion of one spouse's account to the other spouse. Such a transfer won't be subject to taxes. But subsequent withdrawals from an employer-sponsored plan under a QDRO before age 59½ will be subject to a penalty.

Implication: You can give or receive alimony or child support from an employer-sponsored retirement plan, penalty free, as long as those payments are required by a QDRO. Don't take the money out of a plan and then give it to your spouse. The IRS will look harshly on that approach, applying income tax under the theory that you took a distribution. Money should go directly to the beneficiary of the QDRO, as required.

IRA Exceptions

The separation-from-service and QDRO exceptions do not apply to early distributions from IRAs. *On the other hand, there are escape hatches that are only for IRAs...*

• **Higher education.** Distributions from IRAs for post-high-school expenses are exempt from the 10% penalty.

Eligible expenses: Tuition, room and board, fees, books, supplies and necessary equipment. These qualifying expenses can be used to pay for your own education or for the education of your spouse, your children or your grandchildren.

• **Health insurance.** After you are out of work for 12 consecutive weeks, you can take money from an IRA to keep your health insurance in force, penalty free. After you're back at work, you won't owe a penalty on IRA withdrawals used to pay health insurance premiums for the next 60 days.

- **Purchasing a first home.** You may take penalty-free withdrawals up to $10,000 for a first-time home purchase.

Required: You cannot have had an ownership interest in a residence during the previous two years. The $10,000 is a lifetime limit.

- **Military reservist.** If you're called for active duty for at least 180 days or indefinitely, there's no penalty on IRA withdrawals.

Roth IRAs

If you're withdrawing money before age 59½ from a Roth IRA converted from a traditional IRA, you'll owe the penalty on the amount that is attributable to your earnings inside the Roth IRA, but not to your original contributions.

Exceptions: Death, disability and first-time home buyer up to $10,000. *The SEPP solution…*

Some of the exceptions listed above (death, disability, divorce) apply only in specific circumstances. However, IRA owners can make use of the SEPP exception at any time. Participants in other plans can use SEPPs after separation from service. SEPP rules are so flexible that you can take out almost any amount needed, penalty free, as long as your account balance is large enough. thre e methods permitted by the irs…

- **Life expectancy.** You withdraw money based on your life expectancy, according to the IRS tables. For instance, if your life expectancy is 40 years, you would calculate 1⁄40 (2.5%) of your plan balance and withdraw that much each year.

- **Amortization.** You calculate that your initial plan balance will grow by a reasonable rate, perhaps 6% or 7% each year. The higher the assumed rate is, the greater the penalty-free withdrawals permitted. This method allows much higher withdrawals than the life-expectancy method.

- **Annuitization.** This complicated calculation, incorporating annuity factors and present values, allows you to withdraw a bit more than with the amortization method.

Example: You have a $600,000 IRA and you wish to withdraw $2,500 per month. However, if the SEPP rules (amortization method) require that you withdraw $3,750 per month from a $600,000 IRA, you'd be paying tax on an unneeded $1,250 a month.

Solution: Split your $600,000 IRA into a $400,000 IRA and a $200,000 IRA, tax free. Then take distributions from the $400,000 IRA, pulling out the $2,500 per month that you need, using the amortization method. In your other $200,000 IRA, you can continue the tax-free buildup.

James Blinka, CPA , tax partner, BDO Seidman, LLP, Two Plaza E., 330 E. Kilbourn Ave., Milwaukee, Wisconsin 53202.

REPORT #59

The Ultimate Tax-Free Estate Plan

Too many people mistakenly assume that trusts are only for the fabulously wealthy and not for those with just a family home, a company pension and a life insurance policy. But even these people can benefit substantially from what trusts have to offer.

Reason: Trusts save thousands of dollars in gift and estate taxes and provide a way to manage assets when the original owners are no longer available. They also can protect assets from creditors and malpractice suits. Trusts need to be set up properly if they are to be effective, so be sure to consult a knowledgeable attorney. Here are five basic types of trusts and what they can do for you.

1. Life Insurance Trust

Let's say you own your home and have some modest investments, a pension and a $500,000 life insurance policy. If your children are the beneficiaries of this insurance policy, your family could owe the government hundreds of thousands of dollars in additional estate taxes.

Reason: Life insurance proceeds, while not subject to federal income tax, are considered part of your taxable estate and are subject to federal estate tax. (Estates are taxed at a maximum rate of 40% in 2015, with a $5.43 million exclusion.)

Solution: Create an irrevocable life insurance trust which will own the policy and receive the cash payout upon the policy owner's death. *There are several benefits to doing this...*

- **Income for the beneficiaries.** The irrevocable life insurance trust can be structured so that your survivors receive some or all of the annual income generated by the trust. The survivors can even receive the principal—subject to certain restrictions.

- **Avoidance of estate taxes.** If it's properly structured, such a trust ensures that insurance proceeds escape taxation in your estate as well as the estate of your surviving spouse. In addition, because the proceeds are not included in your taxable estate or your spouse's taxable estate, they are not part of the public record and escape publicity. They also are not affected by probate costs.

- **Protection of assets.** The trust protects insurance proceeds from creditors and malpractice actions.

- **Reliable management.** By naming a family member and an outsider, such as a bank or accountant, to manage the trust assets, you eliminate the problem of relying on inexperienced or incapable beneficiaries to handle the trust's money.

2. Credit Shelter Trust

No one can predict the future of estate tax law. In the meantime, take advantage of tax-free exemption amounts. The primary purpose of a credit shelter trust is to preserve the applicable estate-tax exemption that all individuals get in their estates. Under the law, everyone can give away $14,000 to individuals during 2015, and a certain amount during his or her lifetime ($5.43 million), or upon death ($5.43 million) free of tax. Most couples own their property jointly and have wills in which the husband bequeaths everything to the wife and the wife leaves everything to the husband. This might not be best.

Reason: Let's assume that a couple jointly owned an estate worth $7 million. If one of the spouses died in 2009, there would have been no estate tax because of the unlimited marital deduction. But if the second spouse died in 2011, the estate owes a substantial tax bill.

Solution: When your joint estate exceeds twice the applicable exemption amount, divide all the joint property equally between you and your spouse. For example, transform a joint brokerage account into two separate accounts with half of the assets in each. Then create a credit shelter trust under each spouse's will. The trust will allow the estate of each spouse to escape tax by taking maximum advantage of the applicable exemption amount assuming that there are sufficient assets to fund the trust.

Example: When the first spouse dies, the assets valued up to the applicable exemption amount go into a credit shelter trust for the benefit of the second spouse. (When the second spouse dies, those assets pass directly to the children or other heirs, with no estate tax.) Whichever spouse survives can have the right to receive all the income produced by the trust. That spouse also has the right to take principal from the trust to maintain his or her standard of living. It's almost like having the assets in your own name.

Important: It's not enough to just create the trust. Retitle your joint property in separate names so that, upon your death, the property can be transferred to the trust in order for it to save your family additional estate taxes.

3. QTIP Trust

A Qualified Terminable Interest Property (QTIP) trust defers taxes and helps families achieve personal goals. Its aim is to ensure that, after a spouse's death, assets exceeding the applicable exemption amount pass first to the surviving spouse tax free and then to the individuals for whom they are ultimately intended.

Benefit: The trust is often used with second marriages to provide lifelong support for a current spouse. Then, after the second spouse's death, the QTIP funnels assets to the children from the first marriage. Under this arrangement, your current spouse will receive all of the income annually from the trust for life. Even though your spouse's interest in the trust property terminates upon death, the initial transfer of property to the trust still qualifies for the unlimited marital deduction.

4. Grandparents' Trust

This trust is similar to the children's trust, except that the grandparents establish it to help pay for their grandchildren's college expenses. A separate trust can be created for each grandchild. There is a $14,000 per grandparent limit on the amount that can be placed free of gift tax in each trust in 2015 (the $14,000 may be adjusted for inflation in the future). As with a children's trust, the trust document and the trustee define how much money can be used for which purposes.

Important: Avoid setting up a single trust that names more than one grandchild as a beneficiary. Otherwise, you will run into the expensive generation-skipping transfer (or GST) tax.

Note: There have been sweeping changes to the GST so consult a tax expert.

Martin M. Shenkman, CPA and attorney, specializing in trusts and estates in New York City and New Jersey. He is author of more than 40 books, including *The Complete Book of Trusts* (John Wiley & Sons).

Top 10 Big Mistakes When Planning Your Estate

An estate plan should be a clear road map, one that guides your assets to your chosen beneficiaries with a minimum of time and expense. That's what it should be, but too often it's not. Inaction and estate planning blunders can result in disaster for your loved ones.

Consider what could happen: Your estate could fall into the wrong hands...the IRS could end up with far more than its fair share...or your heirs could battle endlessly. *None of this will happen to your estate as long as you avoid the most frequent and damaging planning mistakes...*

1. Not having a will. If you die without one, your assets will be divided according to state law, which may not be the disposition you desire. For example, in some states, your spouse and children split your estate.

2. Focusing solely on taxes. To many people, estate planning is synonymous with tax planning. They reason that since the federal estate tax exemption is $5.43 million in 2015 ($5.45 million in 2016)—they will not owe estate tax and don't need to do any planning.

The size of your estate—taxes or no taxes—should never determine whether you have a comprehensive plan. Most estate-related family disputes are not even about money. They occur because people tend to ignore the human component of estate planning. *Here are some examples...*

- **Heirs may squabble over furniture, inexpensive jewelry, family photographs, etc.**—things you might never think they would fight over.

- **You might name one child as executor,** and inadvertently slight your other children no matter how the assets are divided up.

3. Being mysterious. It may make good TV drama, but there is usually nothing to be gained by keeping heirs totally in the dark about your intentions. Explain your choices to them, and specify your bequests. Give away heirlooms while you're alive— you'll get to see your heirs enjoying them, and they won't have to fight over them later. And, as we've seen in several news stories, it's vital to let your family know what you would want done if difficult medical decisions have to be made.

Strategy: Discussions with family are not legally binding. Neither are personal notes. Include your wishes in formal legal documents to prevent fights. Have a living will drafted stating your health-care wishes. Get a health-care proxy appointing an agent to make decisions.

4. Neglecting to update beneficiary designations. Life insurance policies, retirement accounts, payable-on-death (POD) accounts set up at banks and with brokerage firms, and certain other assets will pass to the beneficiaries you have named in the accounts' paperwork, no matter what it says in your will. You should check periodically to be sure your beneficiary choices in these accounts are current.

After a divorce, for example, you probably won't want your ex-spouse to be the beneficiary of your life insurance or your IRA.

5. Relying on outdated documents. Assets change, families change and the laws change. All of your estate-planning documents—will, trusts, letters of instruction to an executor, power of attorney—should be reviewed at least once every three years...and anytime a relevant law changes.

Example: A common strategy has been to leave the amount of the estate tax exemption to a bypass trust for the children and the balance of the estate to the surviving spouse, since spousal bequests are automatically tax free, but such a plan may leave too much to the kids and too little to your spouse.

6. Naming the wrong executor. After your death, your executor will become the quarterback of your estate plan, responsible for handling all the assets that transfer under your will.

Trap: If you name your spouse, he/she might be too overcome by your death to function well. Similarly, it may not be practical to name your son, who lives across the country.

Strategy: Name a young relative who lives nearby, someone who is well-organized and detail-oriented. If you think that your spouse's feelings will be hurt, designate such a person coexecutor along with your spouse. Whoever you name, make sure to ask him if he is willing to serve. Name two or three backups, too, in case your first choice is unable or unwilling to act.

7. Making things difficult for your executor. If your financial papers are scattered everywhere, handling your estate will be more difficult and time-consuming. Valuable assets (such as life insurance policies) may be overlooked.

Strategy: Keep copies of your documents in one place, such as a looseleaf binder or folder. Write on each copy where the original is located—and let your executor know where the originals can be found—such as with your lawyer, who may have your original will. Simplify things for your executor by consolidating accounts to the extent that is practical.

8. Improper use of joint ownership. As you grow older, you might want to add the name of a relative, such as your daughter, to your bank or brokerage accounts. This joint owner could write checks, handle investments and so on, if you become unable to manage your own affairs.

Trap: Your co-owner will automatically inherit that asset, freezing out all other heirs no matter what's in your will.

Strategy: Instead of joint ownership, give to your trusted friend or relative a durable power of attorney over your accounts.

This person will be able to handle your affairs if need be, yet your will shall remain fully in effect. If you want one younger relative to be able just to write checks for you, name him as joint owner of a checking account where relatively modest sums are maintained.

9. Underestimating the size of your estate. Despite the recent easing of the federal estate tax, some states are increasing their estate taxes. If you leave a sizable estate, chances are that your heirs will owe some tax.

Trap: Even if you don't think of yourself as rich, if you die while owning real estate, life insurance policies and a retirement account, you may be in estate tax territory.

Strategy: Some planning can help reduce the tax burden you'll leave to your loved ones.

Example: In 2016, you can give up to $14,000 per year to any number of recipients with no tax consequences. That number will increase in future years with inflation. You may also want to arrange for insurance on your life to be purchased in a trust if your estate will need cash to cover an expected estate tax bill. Talk to your financial adviser.

10. Not coordinating advisers. Good estate planning involves a variety of skills. Having all your legal documents (will, trusts, etc.) in order may not guarantee a sound estate plan if your life insurance is not handled properly. Similarly, you might need a tax adviser to see if tax planning is necessary and a financial planner to handle your investments.

Key: Make sure all of your advisers know about each other —and about your entire estate plan—so they can work with each other to ensure a happy ending.

Martin M. Shenkman, CPA and attorney, specializing in trusts and estates in New York City and New Jersey. He is author of more than 40 books, including *The Complete Book of Trusts* (John Wiley & Sons).

REPORT #61

Interest Expense Deductions You Never Knew Existed

The best way to minimize the after-tax cost of borrowing is to maximize your deduction for interest expense. *Follow these guide lines...*

Your Debt Portfolio

Start by reviewing your total borrowing and considering it in terms of a "debt portfolio."

Objective: To allocate your total borrowing among different kinds of debt in the manner that gives you the biggest total interest deduction.

Key: Money is "fungible"—no matter how you get it, you can use it for any purpose.

If you want to borrow to finance, say, a consumer purchase, it's not necessary to take out a consumer loan to do so. You can instead borrow to finance some expenditure of another kind—such as an investment or business purchase—and use the cash you save to purchase the consumer item.

Result: Both the amount you borrow and the amount that you spend are unchanged—but you increase your interest deduction by borrowing more money in a manner that produces deductible interest.

Going forward, adjust your debt portfolio by planning new borrowing to be of a type that generates deductible interest.

Also—consider taking advantage of today's low rates to pay off old nondeductible debt, substituting it with new tax-favored financing.

Planning Opportunities

The best planning opportunities for generating interest deductions exist with mortgage interest, investment interest and business interest. College loan interest also is deductible, but the deduction is subject to so many restrictions that planning opportunities for it are limited.

Consumer interest—such as the interest charged on credit cards to finance consumer purchases—is not deductible. Seek to make it as small a part of your debt portfolio as possible. *The deduction rules to use in planning…*

• **Mortgage interest is deductible on up to $1 million of borrowing used to acquire or improve a residence.** The deduction can be divided up between two residences. If you have a vacation home, you can deduct mortgage interest for it as well as for your primary residence. If you have more than two residences, you can claim the deduction for your primary residence and the second residence of your choice—and you can change that choice each year. In addition, interest is tax deductible on up to $100,000 of home-equity borrowing, regardless of the purpose for which the borrowed funds are used.

Rule: To generate deductible mortgage interest, a loan must be secured by a residence. It is not enough to use a loan to buy or improve a home, if the loan is not secured by the home.

• **Investment interest is deductible up to the amount of your net investment income.** That equals your investment income—including dividends, interest and short-term capital gains—minus your investment expenses. Excess investment interest may be carried forward to be deducted in future years, without limitation.

Tactic: If your investment interest expense exceeds investment income, one may elect to treat long-term capital gains as short-term gains and deduct investment income against them.

Doing so yields a current deduction rather than a deferred one—but the deduction produces tax savings at only a maximum 23.8% rate, instead of at higher ordinary tax rates.

Rule: To produce an interest deduction, borrowed funds must be used to purchase an investment and be traceable to it. If you commingle borrowed funds with other funds in your checking account, you may lose the deduction—so keep borrowed investment funds in a segregated account.

• **Business interest** is deductible without limit when incurred as a business expense and reported on your return's Schedule C. You can have this tax deduction if you operate a business proprietorship either full time or as a sideline. If you are an owner of a pass-through entity such as an S corporation, limited liability company or partnership, you should borrow the funds yourself.

Example of debt portfolio planning: Say you intend to purchase a $20,000 automobile for personal use. If you use an auto loan to do so, you will get no interest deduction. But you may be able to obtain an interest deduction by using a $20,000 home-equity loan to buy the vehicle or by borrowing to finance a $20,000 investment or business expenditure instead of paying cash—and using the cash saved to buy the car.

Home Borrowing

This may be your most powerful method of reducing interest cost. Deduction rules are generous, and home-secured loans often carry lower interest rates than other kinds of loans.

Some opportunities...

• **Home-equity borrowing exceeding $100,000** is deductible as...

• Business interest, if the borrowed funds are used for a business purpose.

• Investment interest, if borrowed funds can be traced to the purchase of an investment.

Advantages: By using a home as security for a business or investment loan, you may get a lower interest rate—or obtain funds you couldn't get at all otherwise.

• **Home-equity borrowing up to $100,000 can be used for any purpose.** You can use such loans to refinance expensive and nondeductible credit card debt, or to finance new consumer purchases.

Caution: Beware of paying down your home mortgage too quickly. Many home owners do prepay their mortgages to increase their financial security and reduce the total interest they will pay on the mortgage over the years. But by prepaying your mortgage, you may significantly reduce the total deductible borrowing available to you.

If you prepay a mortgage to the point that equity in your home is in excess of $100,000 (the maximum home-equity loan for which interest is deductible), you will not be able to borrow against the excess with deductible interest even if you need the money. Your home mortgage may just be your least expensive debt after taxes. Other debt, such as credit card debt, may incur much higher rates and not be deductible.

Best: When prepaying debt, start with your most costly debt first. Your home mortgage may be last on the list.

Refinancing

If you increase the amount of the loan outstanding when refinancing a home loan to take advantage of a lower interest rate, deductibility depends on the amount refinanced and how you use the proceeds. If the excess is used to substantially improve the home, it can be treated as acquisition debt (subject to the $1 million limit). If it is used for other purposes (such as to pay off credit card balances), it can be treated as home equity debt (up to the $100,000 limit). Interest on any excess amount is nondeductible.

Example: You have a $300,000 mortgage balance on a home worth $575,000. When refinancing your mortgage to obtain a lower interest rate, you increase the balance to $450,000 and use the excess to pay off credit card debt, as well as other personal expenses. Of that amount, $300,000 (the replacement of your outstanding balance) is treated as deductible acquisition debt, while $100,000 is treated as deductible home equity debt, but interest on the remaining $50,000 is nondeductible.

A loan not secured by a residence does not produce deductible mortgage interest.

Example: Parents lend a child $20,000 to make a down payment on a house. Even though the money is used to buy the home, the child cannot deduct mortgage interest on the loan unless it is secured by the home just as the primary mortgage is.

Investment Borrowing

Deduction rules for investment borrowing are the opposite of the rules for home-equity borrowing—the loan need not be secured by an investment, but it must be spent on an investment—except for tax-exempt securities. If a parent lends funds to a child who uses them to make investments, the child can deduct interest paid to the parent on the loan under normal investment interest rules.

Important: Intrafamily loans must have reasonable terms, be documented and the terms must be followed—or you risk having the IRS treat them as gifts.

Business Borrowing

Interest on this is deductible with no limit if borrowed funds are used for legitimate business purposes. An undocumented loan, or one whose terms are not followed, may be deemed by the IRS to be an equity investment—if this is the case all interest is disallowed.

Note: Borrowing money to buy stock in a business is treated as investment borrowing and the deduction is subject to the investment interest limitations mentioned previously.

The late Gail T. Winawer, CPA , former managing director, American Express Tax and Business Services Inc., New York City.

The Business Travel Loophole the IRS Doesn't Want You to Know

If you're self-employed or run your own company, you have considerable leeway in setting your business travel plans. With some forethought—and a great deal of diligent record keeping—you can legitimately convert leisure travel costs into tax-deductible business expenses.

Domestic Trips

Travel within the United States is deductible if the trip is primarily for business.

Included: Airfare, airport parking, cabs, car rentals, tips.

What makes a trip primarily for business? If you go to Milwaukee to see clients for a week and spend an afternoon playing golf, that's a business trip. The line can be blurred if you mix less business with more pleasure—say, go to San Francisco for a business meal or two, then tour the wine country for the weekend.

Strategy: Make sure that the majority of the days involved are business days. For example, if you're away for a week, include at least four business days. The IRS generally accepts a broad definition of business days (that is, days during which you materially conduct business). You don't need to devote the entire day to business for it to count.

Examples: Days traveling to and from a business trip are business days, as well as weekends and holidays in between weekday business meetings. That's especially true if staying over saves you money.

Saturday night special: Say you have business meetings in Chicago, Monday through Friday, and based on available flights, going home on Sunday gives you a much lower airfare than going home Friday night or Saturday.

Result: You book a return flight on Sunday. Saturday and Sunday count as business days when determining whether your airfare is deductible. The same is true if you have business meetings Friday and the following Monday—you stay the weekend to avoid paying for travel back and forth, so the weekend counts as business days.

Combination Plays

With those ground rules in mind, you can see how to combine business and leisure travel.

Example: You're going to New York City for an industry convention, which will require a total of five business days, including travel.

If you add an extra three or four days to your trip for personal pursuits, the trip still counts as a business trip because the majority of days are used for business, so your travel costs will be fully tax deductible.

Putting pleasure first: Another approach is to decide when and where you would like to vacation, then construct a business trip around that plan by arranging business meetings in that area before you go. As long as more than half of the days can be counted as business days, you can deduct your travel costs, room and board...

In today's world, with frequent-flier miles, transportation outlays may be a minor portion of your overall trip costs.

Significant nontravel expenses: Especially if your business is conducted in major metropolitan areas, hotel and meal costs can easily outstrip airfares. Therefore, the ability to deduct those costs can be very valuable. *What's deductible...*

● **Hotels.** You can deduct the hotel costs incurred for business days—the nights before and after doing business, for instance, and weekend stays that cut travel costs. And, if you take a day off during a week of business meetings, you're unlikely to face a challenge if you deduct all of your hotel bill.

Caution: If you take a business trip and arrive several days early or stay late, just for a vacation, you cannot deduct the hotel costs for these nonbusiness days. Therefore, you might be better off truly mixing your business and pleasure days. Do business at the beginning and the end of your trip. You can make a strong case for deducting hotel days that are bookended by business days.

● **Meals and entertainment.** The Tax Code limits these deductions, as they relate to business meetings and other business contacts, to 50%. So, for every $100 you spend taking contacts to dinner or to basketball games, only $50 can be deducted. Meals you eat by yourself are 50% deductible as well, as long as you eat those meals while away on business.

Travel Companions

You may want to take your spouse or other companion (and perhaps your children) with you on business trips.

Required: For a companion's travel costs to be deductible, he/she must be an employee on your company's payroll, going along for a genuine business purpose. If those conditions are not met, though, you probably can still deduct business-related hotel costs, even if you share the room. In addition, you can take a 50% deduction if you pick up the check for a business meal where spouses are present.

Foreign Travel

The rules are a bit different if you leave the US on business. *If your foreign trip lasts...*

• **Seven days or less,** including one travel day, four business days will make it a business trip—the same as within the US. Your travel expenses are deductible.

• **More than seven days,** then you need to calculate how much time you spend on nonbusiness activities. If you spend at least 25% of the days vacationing, the trip isn't considered a pure business trip. For a week-plus, business/pleasure trip, you need to make an allocation between work and play.

Example: You go to England for a total of 10 days, including three days that involve nothing but sightseeing. You can deduct only 70% of your travel costs.

Strategy: If possible, keep a foreign business trip within the seven-day limit, so your tax write-off will extend to your leisure time, too.

Rely on Records

As mentioned, arranging appointments in advance can help you mix in some vacation time with tax-deductible travel, foreign or domestic.

Key: If it's practical, try to minimize days spent entirely on pleasurable pursuits. A genuine business meeting or attendance at a convention session will make that day a tax-deductible business day, even if you take some time off to play tennis or have a purely social restaurant meal.

Strategy: Make sure to keep thorough records, including phone logs and e-mail correspondence involved in setting up meetings. If you go to a convention, keep a copy of the program and any notes you took during the session.

After your return, send letters or e-mail to the people you met, referring to the business purpose of your encounter. Keep copies, along with any evidence that your business was enhanced by the encounter.

Bottom line: Never hesitate to deduct your legitimate travel and entertainment costs when you prepare your tax return. However, claimed travel and entertainment deductions may attract the attention of IRS agents, so be prepared to justify any deduction. The more paperwork you have showing the business purpose of your travel, the more likely your deductions will be sustained.

Bernie S. Kent, Esq., CPA, former managing director, Telemus Capital, 2 Towne Square, Southfield, Michigan 48076. He is past chairman of the personal financial planning committee of the Michigan Association of Certified Public Accountants.

REPORT #63

Tax Form Loopholes the IRS Doesn't Want You to Know

Most people simply try to get the numbers right when they fill out their tax returns. But there is a lot more to this. Making strategic decisions can save you money, and, if you're careful, can reduce the odds of an IRS audit. *Consider these strategies...*

For Individual Taxpayers

Loophole: **Make a Section 83(b) election when exercising any unvested incentive stock options.** The election has to be made within 30 days of the exercise and will lower your alternative minimum tax (AMT) liability. Making a Section 83(b) election means you owe AMT—in the same year that you make the election—on the difference between the exercise price for the options and the fair market value of the shares. If you don't make the election, the AMT is calculated on the difference between the price you pay for the options and the fair market value of the shares when they vest.

Strategy: If you expect the shares to increase substantially in value, exercise incentive stock options as soon as possible. That way, you minimize the difference between the exercise price and the shares' market value.

Loophole: **File a gift tax return for gifts used to pay insurance premiums**. File the return even though it is not legally required. When you give money to a trust to pay insurance premiums, no gift tax return is required if you give no more than $14,000 in 2015 and 2016 and no grandchildren are involved (as long as the recipient signs a "Crummey" letter, making the payment a gift of a present interest).

If the IRS determines in a subsequent estate tax audit that the letter was inadequate, no statute of limitations will have run out. The donor or his/her estate could be liable for tax on the gifts.

Better: Filing a gift tax return blocks the IRS from assessing taxes after the three-year statute of limitations runs out.

Loophole: **Don't take valuation discounts on Form 709 for small gifts.** When you take a valuation discount for a gift, you must check the box on the gift tax return and include full disclosure of the reasons for the discount.

If you don't take a discount, the box is not checked off and you will decrease the chances of an audit. You should compare the benefits of avoiding an audit with the higher gift valuation.

Loophole: **Enter Form 1099 information on Schedules B and D of your tax return—even if it's wrong.** The IRS crosschecks the totals that are shown on Schedules B and D—reflecting capital gains, dividends and interest income—with the amounts banks, brokers and other payors report on Forms 1099. If the amounts differ, an IRS notice is automatically generated.

If there's a mistake on a 1099: Enter the 1099 figure on your tax return. Then subtract the erroneous amount to end up with your real total. Attach an explanatory letter to your return.

***Loophole:* Make a tardy generation-skipping transfer election.** In general, the grandparents who set up trusts for grandchildren can receive a $5.45 million lifetime exemption in 2016 for their collective gifts. When Form 709 gets filed on time, the value of the gift is determined when the gift (or transfer) was actually made. When you make a late election, the value is determined when you filed the late return and elected to offset the gift's value against the lifetime exemption. So, making a post-April 15 election saves money when the value of the gift decreases after you make it, such as a wholelife insurance policy premium.

Trap: If you don't make a timely election and the insured dies, the full face value of the policy's face could be considered a generation-skipping transfer, which could create an enormous tax bill.

***Loophole:* Keep the total of your money in foreign bank accounts below $10,000.** You must file a Form TD F 90-22.1 when the aggregate of foreign bank accounts in which you hold money and accounts from which you have check-signing power (even though the money is not yours) exceeds $10,000.

Filing the form opens the accounts up for IRS scrutiny. for business taxpayers...

Loophole: Choose a low-audit business code number to put on the company's Schedule C. The IRS targets for audit certain types of businesses and industries. When your business could legitimately fit into more than one category, choose the business code number that is not on the IRS's hit list. For example, a car wash can possibly be called an auto service center.

***Loophole:* Attach an "election schedule" for a controlled group of corporations to the corporation's Form 1120.** When you run a controlled group of corporations (more than one corporation under common ownership), you must attach to the business's tax return an election schedule that includes an apportionment plan for certain tax items (for example, the AMT exemption). Otherwise, the IRS automatically allocates all exemptions and the benefits of the lower tax brackets equally among all the companies in the group.

Strategy: When you have a controlled group that includes dormant and active businesses, allocate all the exemptions and tax breaks to the active business.

***Loophole:* Report a fair market value appraisal on Form 1120S when you switch your C corporation to an S corporation.** This will reduce the taxes owed on any built-in gains. Businesses that convert from C corporation to S corporation status must value the business's assets as of the date of the conversion. If assets are sold within 10 years, profits are realized as if the C status were still in effect to the extent of any built-in gains as of that date, that is, the S corporation pays the tax.

Strategy: When you get a preconversion fair market value appraisal, the valuation is generally lower than what the assets could be sold for, saving taxes if the assets are sold before the 10-year deadline.

Edward Mendlowitz, CPA , partner, WithumSmith+Brown, 1 Spring St., New Brunswick, New Jersey 08901. He is author of various books on taxes, including *The Adviser's Guide to Family Business Succession Planning* (AICPA).

REPORT #64

Pay Zero Tax When Selling Your Home

The home sale capital gain exclusion is limited to $250,000 for taxpayers filing singly and $500,000 for married couples filing jointly. But what happens if your home has appreciated in value by far more than the exclusion amount?

Loophole: There is a way to extract cash from highly appreciated residential property while avoiding the tax that you would pay if you sold it outright. *Here are the details...*

Swap Rather Than Sell

You can defer tax on a home's appreciation by using the like-kind exchange rules that are found in Section 1031 of the Tax Code. These rules allow business or investment property to be traded tax free for another business or investment property. Any potential gain is deferred until the replacement property (the property acquired in the exchange) is subsequently sold.

Requirement: For the exchange of a principal residence to qualify, it's necessary to convert the home to business or investment property.

Refinance and swap: Let's say a single home owner purchased a home for $200,000 that is now worth $2 million—so there's a potential gain of $1.8 million. The home owner can refinance the mortgage to pull out cash, up to the equity in the home. Typically, mortgages are offered on up to 80% of the value of a home after factoring in repayment of any outstanding mortgage.

Assuming this home owner has no mortgage, he/she obtains $1.6 million cash (80% of the $2 million value) by taking a mortgage on the home. Some or all of the money is then used to purchase a new home. Then he rents out the old home, thus converting it to investment property. After a time—typically a year or two to establish the home as an investment property—when the home is worth, say, $2.2 million, he "exchanges" (details below) the now rental property for another like-kind property, which could be a strip mall, an office building, other rental housing or any other investment property worth at least $2.2 million. The like-kind requirements are met because he is exchanging his rental real property for rental real property.

Result: The home owner pockets no cash (remember that at least a $1.6 million mortgage needs to be obtained on the replacement property, and the remaining cash must be used to acquire the replacement property when the home is exchanged) and owns rental property worth $2.2 million or more. And, there are no current taxes on the deal!

IRS Blessing

Can you utilize both the home sale exclusion and Section 1031? The IRS has issued guidance on this point, allowing a home owner to benefit from both the home sale exclusion and the like-kind exchange rules [Revenue Procedure 2005-14]. Under this guidance, a home owner may be able to use the exclusion and the exchange rules to avoid all current tax on an exchange, while increasing the basis of replacement property.

Key: The home owner must have owned and lived in the home for at least two of the five years before the date of the exchange. This is required for the home sale exclusion. Say he lived in the home from 1999 to 2013, and then rented out the place in 2014 and in 2015, the year the home was sold. The home qualifies for the exclusion because the home owner met the two-out-of-five-year requirement and, since it has been converted to rental property, for like-kind exchange treatment as well.

In this example, the IRS views the first $250,000 ($500,000 if married) of the $2 million gain as qualifying for the home sale exclusion (the exclusion must be applied first). The balance of the gain ($1.75 million) is then tax deferred under the likekind exchange rule.

Even better: The home can be depreciated throughout the rental period, yet there will be no depreciation recapture required upon its exchange. Recapture is necessary only when there is a recognized gain. Since the property is exchanged, no gain is recognized.

If the home owner had received cash as part of the exchange —to account for a difference in the value between the exchanged properties—then the gain would have been taxable to the extent of this "boot." Depreciation recapture may affect the tax rate paid on this amount—in this example, it would be 25% instead of the capital gains rate, which can be as high as 23.8%.

Newly Acquired Property

What is the basis in the property acquired in exchange for the old residence? This is important to know for purposes of figuring depreciation on the replacement property.

According to the IRS guidance, the basis of the replacement property is the basis of the relinquished property, increased by the exclusion amount. In effect, the home sale exclusion amount is treated as gain on the exchange, which serves to increase the basis of the replacement property. Recall that in the example above, the basis of the original home was $200,000. Therefore, the basis of the replacement property will be $450,000 (that's $200,000, increased by the excluded gain of $250,000).

The Nitty-Gritty

• **Rules for like-kind exchanges.** It is often difficult for a taxpayer to swap an investment property for another investment property. Additional strict timing rules can make effecting an exchange even more difficult. For these reasons, it may be prudent to use an accommodator, a person who helps complete a deferred exchange. In addition to preparing documents to facilitate an exchange and holding on to the proceeds from escrow, an accommodator, if qualified, will give tax advice on various aspects of the exchange.

How the process works: First, the taxpayer enters into an escrow for the sale of their investment property. Then the accommodator advises the taxpayer about the requirements to successfully complete an exchange and the tax law's time limits. (After the close of escrow, the taxpayer has 45 days in which to identify properties that may be the target of an exchange.

The taxpayer identifies the property in a signed statement delivered to the accommodator. The taxpayer then has 180 days from the close of escrow in which to close on the acquisition of the targeted property.)

Caution: These time limits are very strict. They are not extended even when a deadline day falls on a Saturday, Sunday or holiday. It is the accommodator's job to see that these limits are understood and satisfied.

Note: The taxpayer, and not the accommodator, is responsible for finding the replacement property, which may be done through a real estate agent.

● **Home sale exclusion rules.** If the taxpayer receives a rental residence in an exchange and then subsequently converts it to his principal residence, another home sale exclusion cannot be taken on a future sale of this residence unless a "special use" test is satisfied. Instead of the usual two-year use requirement, a taxpayer who acquires a residence in a like-kind exchange must live in the home for at least two years and own it for five years prior to a future sale to qualify for the exclusion. Also, if there is any nonqualified use of the residence after 2008 (e.g., as a vacation home or rental property), then gain attributable to this nonqualified use will not qualify for the home sale exclusion when the home is eventually sold, even though the tests for ownership and use are met.

C. Anthony Phillips, CPA , president of Downstream Exchange Company, an accommodator of tax-deferred exchanges, in Pasadena, California. He is also a partner in the firm Phillips & Company, a frequent speaker at conferences of the Federation of Exchange Accommodators and a faculty member of the California Association of Realtors.

REPORT #65

$1 Million Tax-free Cash for Your Kids

If you want to make a major bequest to a child or grandchild, the smart way to do it may be to use life insurance instead of a bequest of property. Say you want to leave $1 million to a grand-child. First you need to have at least that much in assets—and, after you take into consideration federal and local estate taxes, you might need twice as much. Also, income earned on the assets is subject to income tax at top rates—and the assets are "tied up." You cannot spend them and bequeath them, too. If you wish to make several such bequests, these problems are multiplied.

Alternative: Fund the bequest to the child with a $1 million life insurance policy held in a life insurance trust. *Why...*

• **A properly structured trust will be estate tax free**—reducing the assets you need by as much as half and cutting the IRS out of the deal.

• **Investment income earned within the insurance policy will be tax free.**

• **The dollar cost is very low since the value of the policy is leveraged through tax savings.**

Example: A married couple, both age 60, find they can buy a $1 million second-to-die life insurance policy (that pays on the death of the survivor) for an annual premium of about $13,000 a year for 15 years. They place the policy in a life insurance trust benefiting a child. Policy premiums are gift tax free, due to the couple's annual joint gift tax exclusion ($28,000 in 2015).

Payoff: The child will receive $1 million tax free at a maximum cash cost to the couple of only $195,000. And the after-tax cost may be as much as 50% less, as the $195,000 is removed from the parents' taxable estate.

Irving L. Blackman, CPA , founding partner of Blackman Kallick, LLP, Chicago. *www.taxsecretsofthewealthy.com*

REPORT #66

Pay Zero Capital Gains for Life

In recent years, investors have learned the risks of holding a "concentrated portfolio." If most or all of your investment holdings were in AIG, Fannie Mae or Lehman Brothers, unexpected events would have suddenly put a whopping dent in your net worth. Diversification reduces your dependence on one stock. To spread your risks, you can sell a large portion of your main holding and reinvest in other companies or mutual funds.

Trap: If your concentrated position consists of highly appreciated shares held in a taxable account, selling will result in a huge tax bill.

Example: You invested $10,000 in The Home Depot many years ago. Now that position is worth $500,000, a large chunk of your net worth. Although you are still upbeat on its prospects, you want to sell the shares to reduce your exposure to one stock. However, selling would trigger a $490,000 capital gain. With capital gains rates as high as 23.8%, the tax obligation could be more than $116,000. Depending on where you live, state and local tax might drive the total tax bill even higher.

Charitable Thoughts

One way to solve this problem is to donate your stock to a charitable remainder trust (CRT) you've created.

Benefits: You would get a large up-front tax deduction. The CRT could sell the shares, tax free, and invest the full amount in a diversified portfolio. (You will be able to direct the investments if you are a trustee of the CRT.) You and perhaps your spouse could receive a lifelong income stream from the CRT, without worrying about reliance on one stock.

Drawbacks: A CRT may be costly to create and maintain. A CRT probably would have to be worth six figures to justify the expense. Ultimately, the CRT assets will pass to charity, not to your heirs, which might be an undesirable result, as far as you're concerned.

Option Plays

If a CRT strategy doesn't appeal to you, another approach is to buy "put" options. Put options on many widely traded stocks are available to individual investors.

How it works: A put option gives the holder the right to sell a particular stock for a set price ("strike price") at a specified time.

Key: If a "European-style" put is purchased, it may not be exercised until the put expires. A two- or three-year put will, therefore, provide tax deferral (you do not pay tax until you sell the stock) as well as downside protection because the put locks in a minimum selling price. During those two or three years, other tax-planning measures may be implemented. You might, for example, harvest capital losses on other assets. Such losses can be accumulated to offset gains—which you may then decide to take on your concentrated position.

Example: You own 5,000 shares of company ABC's stock, now trading at $100 per share. You purchase a put option to sell all 5,000 shares at $90 per share on October 21, 2015. If the stock price is more than $90 per share on that date, you can allow your put option to expire unexercised. Conversely, should the stock price fall below $90 per share, you can exercise your put option and sell your shares.

Outcome: You retain unlimited upside potential for ABC, yet you limit your downside risk to $90 per share, a 10% drop from current pricing.

Putting On a Collar

But be careful—buying a put option can be expensive. If it is not exercised, you'll have spent a sizable amount of money for no tangible result.

Example: You own 10,000 shares of ABC at $50 a share for a total of $500,000. You purchase 10,000 puts at $3 a share for a cost of $30,000. If the price of the stock stays above $3/ share—so you don't exercise the puts—you've lost $30,000 as a result of purchasing them.

Strategy: Sell a call option for your ABC shares, too.

How it works: A call option gives the holder the right to buy a particular stock for a set price at a specified time.

Example: When you buy a put, as above, you also can sell a call on your ABC shares, at, say, $110 per share.

Result: The money you receive for selling the call might offset most or all of the money you pay for the put, depending on market conditions.

You'll wind up with the prospect of selling ABC to the owner of the call, if the stock goes above $110 a share, or using your put option to sell ABC at $90, if the stock falls below that price.

Key: You've now limited your risk as well as your profit potential in the stock. In the language of Wall Street, you have a "collar," between $90 and $110 per share. If the sale proceeds from selling the call completely offset the cost of buying the put, you have a "cashless collar." If either option is exercised, and you sell the stock, you may realize a large taxable gain. For one technique to deal with this gain, see the margin strategy below.

On the Margin

Your collar position is considered a safe asset, so brokerage firms will lend against it. Relatively low-cost "margin" loans will be available for up to 50% of the value of the underlying stock.

Example: With a collar on $500,000 worth of ABC shares, as above, you can borrow up to $250,000 at an interest rate pegged to the broker's rate. That $250,000, in turn, can be used to invest in a diverse portfolio.

Strategy: If you invest in a variety of stocks, you'll probably have winners as well as losers. Winners can be held for untaxed appreciation, while losers can be sold to accumulate capital losses. Ultimately, when you sell your ABC shares and recognize long-term gains, the harvested losses can help to offset the tax on those gains.

Bottom line: If ABC winds up within the $90 to $110 collar when the options expire, you can then enter into another cashless collar.

If the stock goes below $90 or above $110, you'll sell your shares and use the proceeds to repay the margin loan.

Outcome: After a sale and loan repayment, you'll hold a diversified portfolio of stocks so you no longer bear the risk of a concentrated portfolio.

Loophole: Although interest continues to accrue while the loan is outstanding, it's likely that this interest will be tax deductible s an investment interest expense.

Tax Traps

If you enter into a cashless collar, as described above, you must be wary of some potential tax pitfalls...

• **Avoid a "constructive sale."** If you set your collar too tightly, the IRS may argue that you have virtually sold the underlying stock because you have practically eliminated any potential future gain or loss.

Example: With ABC trading at $100, you buy a put for $98 and sell a call at $102.

Result: You may be taxed as if you had actually sold the underlying stock when you entered into the option transactions.

Strategy: In general, there should be at least a 20% difference between the put and call option strike prices.

Example: With a $90 put and a $110 call, as is illustrated above, the $20 difference is 22% of the $90 put price. This probably will be sufficient to avoid a constructive sale.

● **Wait for long-term treatment.** Whenever you enter into a transaction that substantially reduces your risk due to offsetting positions, as in the case of a collar, the holding period for capital gains purposes will depend on how long the underlying stock was previously held.

Long or short: If the underlying stock had been held for more than one year, the capital gain would be long-term when the underlying stock is sold. If the underlying stock had been held for one year or less at the time the collar was entered into, the capital gain would be short-term.

Trap: This short-term treatment would apply no matter when the collar expired. In addition, the previous holding period would be terminated and a new holding period would not start until the collar had expired.

Thus, you would have to hold the stock for more than a year, after the collar expired, to get favorable long-term capital gains treatment.

Key: To circumvent this trap, wait until your holding period is long-term before entering into an options collar.

Robert S. Keebler, CPA , MST, partner, Keebler & Associates, LLP, 420 S. Washington St., Green Bay, Wisconsin 54301. He is author of *A CPA's Guide to Making the Most of the New IRAs* (AICPA).

REPORT #67

Great Stuff at Government Auctions

An IRS Web site lists—with pictures—items that the IRS has seized to settle tax debts and that it plans to auction off.

Examples: Automobiles, business equipment, commercial properties, jewelry, real estate, patents and financial instruments, to name just a few. Recent offerings included homes, sports cars and a small amusement park. Auction dates and locations, and times when the properties can be inspected, are provided. There's also a search engine to help you find the item you are looking for, and a question and- answer explanation of the auction process.

Note : You must attend the auction in person.

More information: Go to *www.treasury.gov/services*.

James Glass, tax attorney based in New York City.

BONUS REPORTS

IRA Rollovers Made Easy

Your IRA may wind up being one of your largest assets, if not the largest. You probably will not accumulate a huge amount from your annual contributions (for 2015 and 2016, $5,500, or $6,500 if you're age 50 or older).

However, money in an employer-sponsored retirement plan can be rolled over to an IRA when you leave that employer, maintaining the tax deferral.

Key: Such rollovers can put you in control of a six- or seven figure investment portfolio. Making the right moves with your rollover can be vital to your financial future. *But it's important to avoid these mistakes...*

Mistake: Taking cash instead of doing a rollover when you change jobs. You may change jobs several times during your career. Often, you'll leave a company where you've participated in a 401(k) or similar retirement plan. In each case, you can roll your account balance into an IRA. Even modest amounts can become meaningful, after numerous years of tax-deferred buildup, when combined this way.

Trap: If you simply take a cash payout from the plan, you'll owe income tax, and a 10% penalty if you're under age 55.

Being human, you might spend what's left, leaving you short of retirement funds.

Mistake: Keeping your money in your former employer's plan. Many companies permit you to keep your money in their 401(k) plans, even after you leave. Some people think a company plan has no or very low fees, or that the investment selections have been carefully screened, so they decide to leave their money behind.

Reality: Employer-sponsored plans often have high fees. You may well cut your costs with a self-directed IRA. Moreover, some 401(k) plans offer good investment choices, but many of them are filled with mediocre funds in only a few asset classes.

Key: With a rollover IRA, you have a virtually unlimited menu of investments. You can spread your wealth cost-effectively among top funds for large-company stocks, real estate stocks, international stocks, various types of bonds, etc.

Mistake: **Keeping your accounts apart.** Over time, if you have left three or four jobs, you may have three or four old 401(k) plans. Plus, you might have an IRA to which you've made annual contributions.

Trap: With the puzzle pieces scattered around, you're making it difficult to put together a cohesive plan. You are more likely to wind up with an unbalanced portfolio, vulnerable to adverse market moves.

Example: At each of your jobs, you have directed 401(k) contributions into growth funds that are heavy in technology stocks. You might not realize that your retirement fund is so exposed to a downturn in one market sector. If you combine all of those tax-deferred accounts into one IRA, record keeping will be simpler. You can easily see what you've got and manage a unified portfolio.

Loophole: The law now permits you to combine all of your tax-deferred accounts, including IRAs to which you've made annual contributions, into one rollover IRA. Combining all of your tax-deferred accounts into one rollover IRA can help you coordinate your entire portfolio for greater tax efficiency.

Example: You want to have a 10% portfolio allocation to real estate investment trusts (REITs) and real estate mutual funds. In a rollover IRA, these securities' high dividend payouts won't be subject to immediate taxation. Concurrently, growth stocks that pay no dividends can be held in a taxable account, where any appreciation eventually will be favorably taxed as long-term capital gain.

Mistake: **Neglecting estate planning.** If you name someone other than your spouse a beneficiary of your retirement account, you have another reason to execute a rollover. Most employer plans call for an immediate payout to a nonspouse beneficiary.

Generally, all the money must be withdrawn (and taxed) right away, or within a few years.

Loophole: That's not as much of a problem with an IRA. A non-spouse beneficiary can stretch out IRA distributions over his/her life expectancy, enjoying valuable tax deferral.

Mistake: **Rolling over employer stock.** In some situations, a partial rollover may be a wise move. That's especially true if you hold a great deal of appreciated employer stock in your account.

Loophole: Such stock can be pulled out of your plan entirely—as opposed to being rolled over—when you leave the company. (Some plans permit in-service withdrawals, after a certain age.) Under the Tax Code, you'll owe tax only on the shares' value when they were contributed to your account.

Example: You're retiring with $500,000 in your company plan, of which $300,000 is in company stock. Those shares were worth $50,000 when they went into your account. You can pull the company shares out of the plan and owe tax on only $50,000. The other $250,000—the net unrealized appreciation, or NUA—will be untaxed until you sell the shares and then the capital gains rate will apply. In the meantime, the other $200,000 in your employer plan can be rolled over to an IRA.

Trap: In the above example, if you do a complete rollover, all of your gains will be taxed as ordinary income at withdrawal. You could wind up paying up to 23.8% to the IRS on capital gains. If the stock is worth less now than when you got it, it makes sense to do a complete rollover.

Mistake: **Taking distributions yourself.** If you decide on an IRA rollover, full or partial, ask that the money be sent directly from your employer to your IRA in a "trustee-to-trustee" transfer. If you receive any funds yourself, your employer must withhold 20%.

Trap: The money withheld will be subject to income tax unless you make up the shortfall out of your own pocket. You may owe a 10% early withdrawal penalty, too.

Example: John Parker, age 48, changes jobs and asks for his $400,000 balance in the company plan to be paid to him. His company withholds $80,000 (20%) and sends him a check for $320,000.

Result: Parker has 60 days to deposit $400,000 into an IRA, completing the rollover. If he puts the $320,000 check into the account, he will pick up $80,000 worth of taxable income. He is under age 55, so he'll also owe an $8,000 (10%) penalty on the amount that's considered withdrawn.

Better way: In a trustee-to-trustee transfer, no withholding is required. You can maintain full tax deferral and avoid the 10% penalty.

Robert S. Keebler, CPA , MST, partner, Keebler & Associates, LLP, 420 S. Washington St., Green Bay, Wisconsin 54301. He is author of *A CPA's Guide to Making the Most of the New IRAs* (AICPA).

The IRS Is Watching!

Credit card companies are helping the IRS catch tax evaders by providing information about customers who have offshore accounts. MasterCard turned over information on 230,000 accounts and American Express agreed to provide similar information. And in 2009, UBS, a Swiss bank, agreed to turn over an unprecedented amount of account information. All of this is part of an IRS program to identify persons who open foreign bank accounts to avoid paying tax on income earned in them.

IRS Press Release.
